WIMSEY THE MANHATTAN BLOODHOUND:

A COMEDY OF MANY ERRORS

By Elizabeth Silverman

&

Maria Szabó

Contents

INTRODUCTION

Once upon a time there was a Bloodhound named Wimsey.

He was an awful dog.

This is his story.

CHAPTER 1--IN THE BEGINNING

You could say that Wimsey's life began somewhat inauspiciously since he wasn't really meant to exist at all.

One day in a small village in Michigan, Jan, a breeder of show bloodhounds, decided to do some shopping in town. She left her husband in charge.

"Don't let the boys into the yard," she warned. "Two of the girls are in heat."

He did.

When two of the males pushed passed him and barreled into the yard he just shrugged. What bloodhounds have in nose they lack in brain so he didn't think they'd be bright enough to know what to do.

They did.

The result was that two months later, eighteen squirming bundles of unplanned bloodhound joy entered the world in need of good homes. It was not a happy occasion.

Six hundred miles away, Maria's life and mine was about to change. I first met Maria when we worked in the same investment bank where she was a sales assistant and I was a biotechnology analyst. We bonded over our mutual love of dogs. People often find their breeds by luck and Maria was no exception. Only in her case, a lot of it. She did what no one is ever supposed to do—she bought a cute puppy in pet store window. Even worse, the puppy was a bloodhound, a breed she knew nothing about.

"What can I say," she told me, "God protects fools." But the pet store puppy was such a hit that a year later she purchased a second one, a female, and this time from a breeder of pet quality bloodhounds. Some people are lucky in love, Maria was lucky in bloodhounds. Both dogs turned out to be healthy and good tempered, although unfortunately, they were still bloodhounds. This meant she could be seen all over the Upper West Side clinging to telephone poles when they decided to go in different directions. And if bloodhounds are dim in the things that matter to us, in the things that matter to them they're canine brainiacs. Like the time Maria returned home to find both dogs covered in flour. She couldn't figure out how they had gotten into it since it was kept on a high shelf. Then she noticed the chair that had been pushed over to the kitchen counter.

By the time old age had claimed both dogs, Maria knew enough about both the breed and its breeders to know that persuading a breeder to sell a dog into a Manhattan apartment was going to be a tough ask. She carefully crafted a detailed, two-page email and anticipated it would take her a year to find a dog. It took two days. As luck would have it, she only had to send it out once and then faster than a bloodhound can run away with your panties in its mouth, she had a contract for a black and tan male puppy. Her email had landed in the inbox of Ramsey Creek Kennels who just happened to have recently co-bred eighteen accidental puppies.

When Maria saw the puppy's kennel name, she knew it was a sign from the Universe. Its name was Ewine and Ramsey Creek's Cuervo Gold, her favorite drink. Nevertheless, she had already picked out a name: Wimsey, after Lord Peter Wimsey, the suave and sophisticated sleuth of Dorothy L. Sayer's classic British pre-war mystery series.

And so it was that fourteen weeks after his unorthodox arrival, Wimsey was driven East (by a well-known show handler, no less) and into Maria's life and ultimately into mine.

Fast forward.

Maria and I had lost touch when we both changed jobs. Then one sunny August morning in Riverside Park, I was sitting in the 82nd Street run with a dog I was fostering for the ASPCA, when the gate opened. A black and tan blur whizzed past me and when I looked up, there was Maria.

"Let's get together!" we exclaimed. But we didn't. Then in February we ran into each other again at the Westminster Kennel Club Dog Show. And now here I was, six weeks later, panting my way up five steep flights to meet her new bloodhound.

The first thing that struck me about Maria's apartment was that it had almost no furniture. She must have seen the look on my face.

"The dogs ate the furniture," she explained. "All except that little loveseat. And that's only because they liked to sleep on it."

The second thing that struck me was Wimsey. All 105 pounds of him.

"Wimsey get down!" Maria cried, and dragged Wimsey off me before he could give me a tracheotomy.

"Sorry about his nails. He won't let me cut them. I think he kind of thinks of them the way Samson thought about his hair."

Maria handed me a towel to wipe away the slobber on my face while Wimsey whacked me painfully in the kneecaps with his powerful tail. I stepped back and took a good look at him. He looked like a cartoon dog. He had a flat head that came to a silly-looking point and all the excess skin on his face dragged down his eyelids and exposed their red rims. It gave him a rather louche and dissipated air, like a jaded French roué who had perhaps spent one too many nights out on the tiles. A large black twitching nose, a pair of long and heavy ears and an elongated, deep-lipped muzzle from which there dangled viscous ropes of drool, completed the picture.

Maria wiped away the drool and used the prominent dewlap that ringed his neck like an Elizabethan ruff to move him out of range.

"Have a seat. I'll get changed and then we can go to the park."

I sat down on the little black loveseat. Wimsey joined me. He rolled over and presented his belly, staring at me in an expectant manner. I started to give him a belly rub when with lightning speed, he drew back his hind legs, placed them firmly against my side and shoved. I went flying through the air like I had been ejected from a catapult. I landed with a thud in the middle of the room.

It was the beginning of a beautiful friendship.

CHAPTER 2--THE BIRTH OF A BOOK

Maria emerged from the bedroom just as I got up from where Wimsey had shot putted me.

"Did Wimsey shove you off the couch? I forgot to tell you he likes to do that."

She removed a heavy prong collar from a hook on the wall and clipped it around Wimsey's neck. In spite of its formidable looking appearance, it seemed to do little to deter him from trying to kill her on the stairs. He flew down them with the stomach-churning speed of a canine Pegasus in pursuit of a juicy sirloin. Once out the door, he hung a hard right and dragged Maria off in the direction of Central Park. As I trotted behind them--Maria had at least four inches on me and very long legs which apparently came in handy--I could see that she had managed to stop him at the corner. But stopped didn't mean silent. He was emitting an odd squeaky noise that sounded more like a rusty hinge badly in need of some oil than anything that should be coming out of a dog. But before I could inquire about it further, Wimsey raised his nose to the heavens and began to bellow like a bull elephant in a bad mood. The sound waves vibrated painfully in my eardrums.

"Wimsey doesn't like red lights," Maria explained. "He thinks that if he bays at them they'll turn green. Which of course they always do."

I wasn't the only one who was curious about Wimsey's unorthodox traffic control system. People came running to see what the ruckus was about. Those closest to him got more than they bargained for since it seemed to be a requirement that each bay be followed up by a shake of the head that sent arcs of viscous spit flying through the air. I had known Wimsey all of fifteen minutes and already he had attempted to puncture my windpipe, break my kneecaps, catapult me off a couch, murder Maria on the stairs, damage my eardrums and give innocent pedestrians a bath. I wondered what he'd do if he had more time.

The next Saturday Maria and I arranged to meet in front of a local diner before my volunteer shift at the ASPCA. I was just paying the bill when I heard a commotion erupt outside, only this time it was less bull elephant and more *Cool Hand Luke.*

"As soon as Wimsey and I were out the door, he picked up your scent and dragged me up Amsterdam Avenue to the front of the restaurant," Maria called out to me from the middle of the assembled crowd.

Wimsey was announcing his "find" to neighborhood.

I quickly had two paws the size of hands on my shoulders and a pair of tonsils in my face. Wimsey bayed and shook so many times that by the time Maria dragged him off of me I looked like a Christmas tree that had been over enthusiastically decorated with tinsel.

The crowd squealed with delight.

"Why don't you let me walk Wimsey this time," I suggested as we extricated ourselves and headed towards the Park. "I'm sure your shoulder could use a break."

She handed me his leash.

Walking Wimsey was like water skiing without the skis. He didn't so much walk as drag, tow and tractor.

I decided to do something about it.

I had a lot of experience handling and training shelter dogs who were large, powerful and difficult to walk, so I didn't think I'd have any trouble with Wimsey. Maria always walked him on a short leash but I thought that if he had more freedom to follow scent, he'd pull less. The following Saturday I brought along a twenty foot training leash. Wimsey liked his new leash. He used it to drag, tow and tractor twenty feet ahead of me.

Watching me walk Wimsey on a twenty-foot leash proved almost as popular as watching me get a slime bath at the diner. "Who's walking who?" people called out, snickering as we skijored by.

It was a rhetorical question.

In spite of my obvious inability to curb Wimsey's dynamic walking style, I nevertheless really enjoyed walking him. I was fascinated by all the attention he received. Whether it was watching him bay at traffic lights or get the better of me on a long leash or even just walk down the street, I had never seen anything like it. Wimsey drew crowds like a magnet drew metal. People ran through traffic to meet him, they honked and waved and took so many pictures of him that it was like being on the red carpet with a Kardashian. And then there was the food. People bought him sandwiches, shared slices of pizza and their lunch bags were his lunch bags. The owner of the corner bodega always sprinted out with a slice of ham whenever he passed by.

"Has it always been like this?" I asked Maria one day when a ten minute walk to the Park turned into an hour because of all the people who wanted to meet Wimsey.

"Yes, always," she replied. "But funny enough nothing like this ever happened with my other two. It's definitely something about him."

"I think it's called charisma." I said.

It gave me an idea.

"Since people like him so much, why don't we write a book?"

"What kind of book?"

I thought for a minute.

"How about a children's guidebook to New York City. Wimsey could be the tour guide and we could take photographs of him doing cute tricks in front of tourist attractions."

Maria liked the idea.

Now all I had to do was teach Wimsey to do cute tricks.

CHAPTER 3--TRAINING CAMP

I quickly came to appreciate that coming up with a good idea and coming up with a good idea that is executable are two very different things entirely. For a start, Maria's need to make a living in order to keep Wimsey in kibble and toys significantly limited her ability to act as the project's photographer and my hunt for a replacement who liked dogs, didn't mind the flying drool in the face aspect of the job and could also work on spec or for very little money seemed to be a fool's errand. I was understandably elated, therefore, when I miraculously found Jay through a fellow volunteer at the ASPCA. My elation was short-lived.

When Wimsey was six months old, Maria had taken him to Diane, the show handler who had driven him East to see if he was show material.

"I think I can show Wimsey to a championship," Diane declared after inspecting him.

Soon thereafter Wimsey began his show career and he had even earned a few points towards his championship when Diane called with some bad news.

"I can't show Wimsey for a while," she announced. "He's had a growth spurt. He looks like a tube sock."

But no sooner had I found Jay than Wimsey's tube sock phase abruptly ended and he and Diane embarked on an extended tour of dog shows up and down the East Coast.

It wasn't until shortly after Labor Day, a full three months after I had the idea for the book, that Maria rang. I could hear the excitement in her voice.

"Wimsey and Diane have done it! My boy is now officially Champion Ewine Rmzy Creek's Wimsey! He's all yours."

"Congratulations!" I replied, "I'll get started right away teaching him the tricks for the first photo shoot."

There was silence at the other end of the line.

"You do know that Wimsey only graduated from puppy school because they were afraid he'd come back, right?"

"I'm sure I'll manage," I replied smugly. After all, I had tons of experience training shelter dogs so how difficult could Wimsey be?

"OK," she said. "I'm sure it will be fun."

It wasn't.

The following Tuesday afternoon I climbed the stairs to Maria's apartment abundantly supplied with both confidence and training turkey. The trick I had in mind for today's lesson was ridiculously simple. Our first shoot was at the Carousel in Central Park and since it had an equine theme I thought it would be cute for Wimsey to hold my riding crop in his mouth. He carried sticks around all the time so I thought he'd really like one made of leather.

Wimsey greeted my unexpected arrival with all the restraint of a cannonball. When he had finished trying to topple me he ran his large, wet nose up and down each of my legs, front to back, back to front, in the manner of an overzealous TSA officer. Having satisfied himself that I hadn't been doing anything exceptionally interesting, like harboring racoons in my apartment, he moved on to my treat pouch which he began to poke at like it was a Pez dispenser.

I took the riding crop out of my backpack and showed it to him. I planned to teach him the take it/ drop it commands and lengthen the time until the "drop it" so Jay would have plenty of time to take photographs. Wimsey looked at the crop, sniffed at it in an unusually perfunctory way and then made it clear that the only thing he was interested in taking into his mouth was the turkey in my treat pouch.

"Wimsey, take it," I said, and opened his mouth and put the stick inside. It clattered to the floor. I tried a few more times but the same thing happened. He obviously had the "drop it" down pat.

I picked up the stick and this time I held it in place. I praised him extravagantly. Then I removed the stick and gave him a piece of turkey. I repeated this a few more times so he would associate the holding of the stick with the getting of the turkey. But the only thing on Wimsey's mind had nothing to do with sticks. He reviewed the situation and came to the conclusion that it would be much more efficient to cut out the middleman. He pushed the stick aside and launched himself directly at my treat pouch. When this failed to achieve the desired result, he bayed at me like I was a traffic light that needed changing.

Clearly I needed to make the stick more interesting. I smeared it with cream cheese, which Maria had assured me was one of Wimsey's favorite foods. Wimsey followed the smearing process with great interest.

"Look, Wimsey, yummy cream cheese," I cooed. Wimsey approached the stick, sniffed at it and then began to delicately lick the cream cheese like an overly polite frog.

"Wimsey take it," I said. I placed the stick in his dripping mouth. It fell to the floor. Then he bent down to resume cream cheese removal operations. I picked it up.

"Wimsey, take it," I repeated, and this time I held the stick in his mouth. I could see his tongue working vigorously.

"Wimsey, drop it," I said and removed the stick. His tongue remained attached. But at least he wasn't baying at me.

I tried peanut butter but it too was a miserable failure. Still I refused to be discouraged. I accepted for the moment that the stick wasn't happening. Perhaps I was going too fast for him. I looked at his pointy head and decided that we should go back to basics. Since Wimsey had, at least in principle, been to puppy school I thought that a refresher course would be helpful. I decided to start with sit-stays which would also be needed for the photo shoots.

"Wimsey, sit," I said firmly. I could see the wheels turning as he evaluated whether or not there were more enjoyable options at his disposal. I waited patiently while he contemplated this thorny question. He finally came to the conclusion that there weren't. He sat. I held up my hand, palm outward in the manner of a traffic cop.

"Stay," I said and took a step backwards.

"Good boy!" I cried and quickly walked forward to reward him with a piece of turkey. This was Dog Training 101--- I was going to gradually lengthen the interval until he got the turkey so he would learn to stay put for increasing periods of time. If he got up, there would be no turkey and we would begin again. Even Wimsey should be able to grasp the idea that if he stayed seated he would get the turkey.

And it was working. I was just congratulating myself on his getting the hang of it, when all of a sudden he erupted with what would have been translated as "expletive deleted" had there been subtitles. Then he launched himself at the turkey.

We began again.

Two good repetitions. Launch.

Five good repetitions. Launch.

One good repetition. Launch.

Three good repetitions. Launch.

I don't know exactly when it was that it dawned on me that the number of sit-stays I could get out of him before he cannoned into me was totally random. It had absolutely nothing to do with Wimsey learning anything and everything to do with just how much patience he was willing to expend at any given time. I was flummoxed. I had trained "smart" dogs who made a quick association between their behavior and a reward. I had trained less intelligent dogs who required many repetitions to make the association between their behavior and a reward. But never before had I met a dog who made NO association between his behavior and a reward.

I hastily revised my artistic vision for the book.

CHAPTER 4--FIRST PHOTOSHOOT

The day of our first photoshoot dawned bright and sunny. In spite of Wimsey's training issues, I was excited as I mounted the stairs to Maria's apartment armed with an entire package of turkey and a backpack stuffed with photography permits, props, Wimsey's favorite squeaky toy, cream cheese and a department store's worth of spit towels.

But spit was the least of the hazards I faced these days. Wimsey now tipped the scales at a bulldozerish 115 lbs. ("He's bigger!" Maria moaned at the start of virtually every conversation). Since bloodhounds can continue to increase in size for a full three years we apparently had a lot more Wimsey to look forward to. I had learned to open the door quickly and advance to the center of the room to cut down on his forward momentum and mitigate the effects of his effusive expressions of hospitality. I pointed a finger at the little black loveseat.

"Couch!" I commanded. It was my one training triumph. Wimsey took to couch training with an alacrity that initially astonished me until I realized that what I had really taught him was simply a much quicker and more efficient means to access to my face and smear it with slobber. I was happy that I had finally taught him something he found useful.

I waited patiently for Wimsey to finish my facial, which, however messy, was still preferable to the alternative. And although I had survived his welcome, surviving a trip down the stairs with him these days was a much trickier proposition. The heart thumping nature of the enterprise had recently grown much more so because Wimsey had decided that the bottom five steps of each flight were surplus to his requirements and he soared over them like a hawk riding a thermal.

Fortunately we--meaning me--managed to make it down the stairs and out the door relatively unscathed where Jay was already waiting for us. Wimsey liked Jay. He barreled into him, bayed in his face, and smacked him in the kneecaps with his wagging tail. Then he took off for Central Park as fast as his four legs could drag me.

Our destination was the Carousel where Wimsey's revised assignment was now to sit next to my crop and riding hat. I arranged the props artistically on the ground and placed Wimsey next to them.

"Wimsey, sit," I said. Wimsey stared at me. I took out a piece of turkey. Wimsey sat.

I backed away.

Jay lifted his camera. Wimsey decided that his nose was dry and badly in need of some serious moisture. He began to lick it. We waited. When he had restored his nose to an acceptably moist and glowing condition, Jay again lifted his camera. Wimsey discovered that he had an itch behind his right ear. He began to scratch it. We waited.

When he was done scratching, Jay lifted his camera. Wimsey decided he was bored. He got up and left.

Jay lowered his camera and I retrieved Wimsey who was engaged in a mesmerizing examination of a rock and put him back in place. Jay lifted his camera. Wimsey lifted his nose. He began to sniff energetically at a passing air current. Jay had a view of him that consisted largely of nostril.

"Can you get him to lower his head?" Jay asked. I took out a piece of turkey and lured his head down from the vertical. I guess I went too far. Wimsey hunched his shoulders and dropped his head between them in a way suggestive of a previously undiscovered species of vulture.

I managed to bribe Wimsey back into a less ornithological-looking position, but no matter how much I cooed at him or squealed his name, he seemed to find a great many things of a fascinating nature located either to his right, to his left or on the ground. Periodically, he interrupted looking at things that were not the camera to stare at me and bay because I hadn't fed him any turkey recently. And if I failed to do it quickly enough, he glared at me like I was a waiter who had forgotten to bring the bread and stalked out of frame.

Not for the first time did I reflect on how ironic is was that I had been worried that Wimsey's face would lack expression. Now I wished it did. Whenever Jay's camera was anywhere in the vicinity Wimsey demonstrated a remarkable ability to arrange his face into an array of glares and stares or looks of skepticism, annoyance or disdain. And he possessed a wicked and cynical side eye that any New York actor would envy. In fact, Wimsey had an extraordinarily expressive face. Just not one that belonged in a children's book.

We gave up and moved on to the statue of Balto where I hoped we would have better luck.

The statue of Balto is perched atop a craggy rock that overlooks a busy park path and we quickly acquired an audience as we set up for the first shot, the easier of the two I had planned. All Wimsey had to do was to stand at the base of the statute and mimic Balto's stance. Since he was a show dog he should be accustomed to having his legs adjusted. But as soon as I started to mess with them he made it clear that Central Park was not a show ring. He scampered up the craggy rock like a chamois of the Alps.

"I guess we're doing the shot of Wimsey kissing Balto first," I called out to Jay, as I followed Wimsey up the rock clutching a tub of cream cheese. I placed a bit of it on my finger to distract him from the nasal analysis of air currents in which he was currently engrossed. Wimsey sniffed at the cream cheese and then began to lick it keeping a suspicious eye on me. Having established that there was cream cheese in the neighborhood, I placed some strategic dots of it around Balto's face. Then I cued Jay and hopped down to await the appearance of the ubiquitous Wimsey tongue so inconveniently evident at the Carousel. I hoped it would be quick. I was afraid a Park Ranger might pop up and I was fairly certain that none of my permits allowed me to turn Balto into a bagel.

Wimsey, however, didn't care about Park Rangers any more than he cared about the white blobs I had so carefully placed on Balto's face. He studiously ignored them. His audience snickered appreciatively. Everyone loves a bad dog as long as it belongs to someone else.

"Maybe he doesn't know it's there," Jay suggested. I looked at him.

"He's a bloodhound!" I exclaimed. "I'm pretty sure he does."

"Well, got any other ideas? I think Balto is off the menu."

I thought for a minute while Wimsey occupied himself watching some birds who were twittering in a nearby tree.

"Maybe he'll lick Balto if he smells like turkey," I said. I went back up and polished Balto's face with a piece of it.

Attracted by the smell, Wimsey approached. Jay lifted his camera. Wimsey shoved his face into Balto's and inhaled deeply. Jay's camera clicked. The picture was more of a sniff than a kiss but at this point the fact that Jay got anything was cause for wild celebration.

But we still needed to get the first shot and although what goes up must come down, Wimsey clearly believed that this did not apply to him. He sensed that whatever awaited him below was not something he was going to like. He resumed his analysis of air currents.

I took out some of my rapidly dwindling turkey.

Getting Wimsey down was one thing, keeping him down was another. As soon as I began to fiddle with his feet, back up he went. I stood on his leash. He was not happy. Every time I fought his feet into exactly the right position, he looked directly at the camera and narrowed his eyes into the annoyed slits he usually reserved for something exceptionally heinous, like the appearance of his Gentle Leader. Then he bayed.

If the Wimsey photography bar had been set any lower by the time we got to the Zoo and Belvedere Castle, it would have been subterranean. At that point all I wanted him to do was to sit (or stand) and not display his profile, his nostrils, his vulture imitation, sniff the ground, examine his toenails, refurbish his nose, bay, scratch himself or look like he ate small children for breakfast.

Nevertheless, when we arrived at Lincoln Center I had no doubt that I was finally going to get Wimsey to do what I wanted him to do. This was because what I wanted him to do was something that I hadn't wanted him to do everywhere else. Bay. I wanted him to bay in front of the Lincoln Center Fountain with the concert halls rising in the background. Getting Wimsey to bay was never a problem. It was getting him to stop that was. All I had to do was to do something that annoyed him. It did not appear to be an insurmountable problem.

I pushed Wimsey into position and gave him the hand signal to stay, something that had been infuriating him all day. Wimsey stared at me in stony silence. I took out a piece of turkey and waved it enticingly just out of camera range. Wimsey stared at the turkey. Then he launched himself at it with the silence of a canine ninja.

Desperate times call for desperate measures. I had one more weapon in my arsenal but I knew from previous experience that it was a dangerous one. It was with the utmost reluctance, therefore, that I removed Squeaky Teddy from my backpack. It was a toy with which Wimsey could charitably be said to harbor an obsessive relationship.

This final provocation proved to be too much for him. He reared up like a stallion, emitted a bay like a thunderclap and 115 pounds of frenzied and outraged hound slammed into me with the force of a freight train.

Jay got his shot, Wimsey got his bear and I got a very bruised backside.

CHAPTER 5--HOUNDUS REX

The American Museum of Natural History was high on my list of popular New York City attractions and since Wimsey wasn't permitted inside (although it never stopped him from trying) it was a challenge to come up with an appealing outdoor concept that I might actually be able to get him to do.

Although my track record in convincing Wimsey to hold anything in his mouth was negligible in the extreme, I thought he might be willing to make an exception for something truly desirable, like a stuffed dinosaur. Wimsey was an avid collector of stuffed toys, the only downside being that they generally met a messy and eviscerated end on the living room floor. He did, however, spare two stuffies, Doggy and Lamby, so I just needed to find a dinosaur that he thought deserved to live. But like so many other things concerning the book, finding the right dinosaur proved to be much more difficult than I had originally anticipated. It turns out that accurate looking stuffed dinosaurs were not in plentiful supply, let alone ones that were large enough to be identifiable as such once they took up residence in Wimsey's cavernous mouth. Wimsey's mouth, much like Mary Poppins' carpet bag, appeared to have an unlimited capacity. Toys, tennis balls, socks, sandwiches and other items of a miscellaneous nature had been known to vanish into invisibility within only to make a surprise reappearance at some later date and in some inconvenient location.

After a lengthy online search, I was finally lucky enough to locate an educational stuffed dinosaur in the form of a rather pricey articulated gray diplodocus. It was similar looking to a brontosaurus and had the same long neck and tail. Although the dinosaur was not quite as large as I had hoped, I thought that if Wimsey grabbed it by its midsection its distinctive neck and tail would be visible enough to make its identity obvious.

On a frosty morning in December I packed up my prehistoric prize and set off to pick up the star of the show. Much to my dismay, if Wimsey was frisky in the fall, in winter he was positively wild.

"Maybe we should take him to Central Park for a while and see if that will calm him down," I suggested as the exuberance of his greeting left Jay somewhat the worse for wear. One hour of vigorous exercise later, he was still happily bouncing and baying at the end of his leash. At least today's shoot would be short and easy.

We arrived at the museum where Wimsey barreled past the statue of Teddy Roosevelt and charged up the stairs like they were San Juan Hill. No doubt he wished to take a closer look at all the bones he could smell inside. I dragged him baying and bucking like a bronco away from the door and into position in front of the museum. Then, when most of him was finally pointing in the right direction, I reached into my backpack and casually pulled out the diplodocus. The effect was electric. Wimsey sprang at it like a cheetah.

I dodged and quickly shoved the dinosaur back out of sight. Wimsey danced and pranced around my backpack like it was a maypole. I began feeding him some turkey and when he seemed to be of a less active disposition I moved him back into position. This time I gave him no time to react. I pulled out the dinosaur, stuffed its midsection into his mouth and jumped out of camera range. When I turned around it was dangling gruesomely by the neck. But only for the second it took Wimsey to drop to the ground so he could shred it.

I darted forward to its rescue but when I made a grab for it Wimsey wasn't having it. He turned his head away from my hand in a way that made it clear that a hound in possession of a stuffed diplodocus was a hound who was going to stay in possession of a stuffed diplodocus. I took out some more turkey. I could see the conflict raging in his head. Then he executed a lightening feint at the turkey while trying to simultaneously keep the dinosaur in his mouth while I executed a lightening feint at the dinosaur while trying to simultaneously keep my fingers still attached to my hand. In this case my hand was quicker than his mouth. I wasn't getting useful picture for the book but I was certainly developing great reflexes trying to. Wimsey, meanwhile, swallowed the turkey and then began to let everyone in the neighborhood know exactly what he thought of me.

I tried again. And again. And then again some more. No matter how many times I positioned the dinosaur, Wimsey repositioned it so that it dangled from his mouth. Mostly this was by its neck but sometimes he introduced an equally macabre variation and dangled it by its tail. If dinosaur dangling were a sport, Wimsey would be a champion. Either way, it looked far too much like he had a dead animal clenched in his jaws for inclusion in a book, let alone one aimed at children. The only time I was able to get him to hold the dinosaur by its midsection, he hunched his shoulders and dropped his head so he resembled a vulture in possession of an exceptionally tasty piece of carrion.

Jay lowered his camera. It was a good thing he was both patient and had an excellent sense of humor, although it would have been nice if Wimsey didn't find ways to amuse him quite so much.

"Any ideas?" he asked. "I don't think he wants to hold the dinosaur the way you want him to" He was also a master of understatement.

"Give me a minute. There has to be something I can get him to do."

"If you say so," he replied with a grin.

Then it came to me. What had Wimsey been doing when he wasn't sitting and dinosaur dangling? He had been jumping, lunging and snatching.

"If I toss the dinosaur in the air do you think you can get a picture of him jumping for it? He might even grab it by the midsection by mistake."

"Let's give it a try" Jay replied.

I flashed the dinosaur at Wimsey and then tossed it high into the air. Wimsey watched the toy's trajectory, drew a bead on its position and then launched himself upwards like a duck breaking cover. We had ourselves a dinosaur picture!

"I think it's better than the one you wanted," Jay observed as he showed it to me.

"You're right, but fortunately he doesn't know it," I replied as I looked at Wimsey. Wimsey looked back at me. The dinosaur was once again dangling out of his mouth.

CHAPTER 6--A HOUND WITH HIS FEET ON THE GROUND

A few weeks after Wimsey's dinosaur escapade, I happened to be with Maria when she opened her mailbox. Inside there was a letter from the Westminster Kennel Club. She tore it open.

"He's in!!!" she cried, her voice quivering with excitement. "Wimsey is going to Westminster!"

We bounded up the stairs, threw open the door and for once it was our turn to be all over Wimsey rather than the reverse. Wimsey didn't precisely understand what all the fuss was about but he definitely knew that he was its focus, although when it came to events of an exciting nature, he usually was.

I thought Wimsey's Westminster adventure would make a good addition to the book so I added a pre-event shoot in front of Madison Square Garden to our schedule. I also blanketed New York media with what I hoped were punchy press releases conveying the thrilling news that Wimsey, New York's hometown hound and aspiring children's book author, would be competing in his first Westminster.

My missives hit their mark and it looked like Wimsey was going to be busy in the weeks leading up to the show—a reporter from *The New York Post* had requested an interview and a film maker wanted to feature him in a documentary about the lives of urban dogs. Since I wanted to get as much work done on the book before his calendar got too full I decided to jump ahead to the shoots in Midtown Manhattan.

I quickly discovered that strolling down streets densely packed with well-dressed pedestrians while hanging onto a hound whose principal mission in life was to distribute his bodily fluids to as wide an audience as possible was the very opposite of a relaxing experience. Every excursion required both extreme vigilance and the eye of an eagle since even a passing brush with Wimsey might bestow the unwelcome gift of hair, drool, and hound smell upon its unlucky recipient. There was also the problem of trying to manage Wimsey's persistent desire to share the contents of his inexhaustible bladder with every building, car, tree, pole and trash bag in Midtown. The neighborhood was one a giant urinal as far as he was concerned. A puddle in the park is one thing, a puddle against the side of a posh hotel was something else entirely. And the situation with respect to his solid waste was even more embarrassing. Wimsey had a real talent for depositing his poop in places inimical to its retrieval. He liked to poop through fences (especially the one onto the West Side Highway), or in bushes (especially the ones with thorns), or down hills, or under dense ivy, or in deep puddles or camouflaged amidst similarly colored vegetation. He was endlessly creative. In Midtown he discovered many more lampposts into whose decorative ridges he could push it and many more people trying to enter or exit a car or a building in front of whom he could deposit it. And the prospect of doing some leisurely business at the curb in full view of people trying to eat lunch at a busy outdoor café was always an enjoyable one. There were also a large number of idling, limo service SUVs whose running boards

Wimsey believed should be used for purposes for which they hadn't been designed. I gave these a very wide berth.

And if Wimsey created a sensation when he bayed and dragged his way through the Upper West Side, it was but a shadow of the stir he created when he bayed and dragged his way down Fifth Avenue. He found the acoustics created by the canyons of stone that surrounded us particularly enjoyable and I have seldom felt so conspicuous. Everyone from harried businessmen to overbooked tourists (I learned to say, "Be careful, he drools," in a host of new languages) stopped to gawk at us, take pictures of us, smile at us or run away from us, depending upon their views with respect to small women with large hounds. Yet amazingly, even amid all these distractions, Wimsey remained focused on what he was there to do. Which was to not do anything that I wanted him to.

Our shoot at Rockefeller Center was a prime example. I wanted a simple picture of Wimsey watching the ice skaters. I had discovered a perfect spot that not only overlooked the ice but also had a convenient rail for him to prop himself with to get a better view. Wimsey liked standing on his hind legs. Whenever he saw a railing or a fence he would drag me over to it and stand up to see what was on the other side. The same applied to counters. In a store he stood up against the checkout counter to see if anyone cared to feed him a snack and at the vet's office he stood up against the receptionist's counter to let her know he had arrived for his appointment. And he stood up against me to bay in my face and make sure that I had heard him.

I showed Wimsey the rail and waited for him to use it as he usually did to see if there was anything going on below that he should know about. Wimsey was an inveterate busybody and if people were doing something, he wanted to find out what. Wimsey approached the rail. He sniffed it. Then he sniffed the area around the rail. Then he sniffed the posts that supported the rail. Then he decided he wished to sniff things wholly unconnected to the rail. He bayed.

"Wimsey, up!" I said and patted the rail in an encouraging manner. Wimsey stared at me like I had asked him to solve a quadratic equation. Then he bayed even louder. I pulled him back over to the rail and although he glanced at the skaters in a way that gave me hope, all four feet remained resolutely stuck to the ground like they had been glued there. I wrapped my arms around his extensive midsection and hoisted. I placed his front feet on the rail. They slid off like they had been greased. And they continued to slide off like they been greased every other time I put them there.

I rummaged in my treat pouch for some turkey. Suddenly I had Wimsey's full and undivided attention. He watched as I held a handful of it just over the rail and it was the work of a New York nanosecond for him to stand up, grab the turkey and slide back down again.

By some miracle Jay managed to get a picture. Clearly I wasn't the only one whose reflexes were improving.

We moved on.

Our next stop was Times Square, where Wimsey thought it imperative that he greet all the tourists with his back to the camera. No amount of cajoling could convince him to do otherwise.

"He's probably annoyed at you for getting that that picture of him at Rockefeller Center," I suggested. "Let's go back to Central Park and see if he'll forgive you enough to let you do some re-shoots."

Wimsey liked this idea so much that we found ourselves nearing Central Park almost as fast as it took him to grab a piece of turkey and slide off a rail. We crossed Central Park West, a street that is bordered on the Central Park side by a high stone wall. Wimsey dragged me over to the wall, side-eyed me to make sure he had my full attention and then very deliberately, he stood up on his hind legs and placed his front feet firmly on top of it.

He settled in for a long stay.

CHAPTER 7--THE PR MACHINE CRANKS UP

The week before Westminster we hit public relations pay dirt. CBS emailed me with the heart thumping news that they wanted to do a feature on Wimsey! They planned to send TV correspondent Morry Alter and his camera crew to tag along on a couple of Wimsey's photo shoots and then do an interview with Wimsey's owner at home. I showed Maria the email.

"I'm not Wimsey's owner, I'm his human," was her comment after she stopped freaking out about doing a TV interview. I tactfully refrained from pointing out to her that she was Wimsey's human in much the same way that Squeaky Teddy was Wimsey's bear.

We began to ponder to which of the many locations on my relentlessly growing shoot and re-shoot list I should subject the CBS crew. We considered the Metropolitan Museum of Art as we fitted Wimsey with the artistic beret that I wanted him to wear for his upcoming visit. It was not going well. The hat spent more time in Wimsey's mouth than on his head and even when it was where we wanted it, it was obvious that a flat and pointy head was not an ideal substrate for a beret. It either slid over his eye or sat on top of him in a way that made him look like he was wearing a large black pancake. Maria finally wrestled the hat away from him for the umpteenth time, grabbed a pair of scissors and added ear holes, a sartorial development that met with Wimsey's immediate and violent displeasure. He flung himself about her apartment like he was possessed and made frenzied attempts to rid himself of the parasite that had attached itself to his head.

"I think we can take the Museum out of the running," I said.

After some lengthy deliberations we settled on Grand Central Station. Wimsey had been there before and it seemed to offer the least amount of scope for any unfortunate occurrences. The size of the main hall meant that I could, at least in theory, hustle Wimsey out of sliming range of anyone just trying to catch a train and Wimsey liked the acoustics. On his previous visit they had inspired his robust baritone* to soar to heights that I was certain would attract TV-worthy crowds.

* Wimsey's vocal register was always a matter of some debate among the many professional musicians who stopped to listen to him. Some declared him to be a true baritone while others insisted he was actually a bass-baritone. The difference of opinion probably depended on whether he was saying hello or demanding my ice cream.

The morning of the shoot Wimsey seemed to sense that an event of an exciting nature was about to unfold. He cut such an enthusiastic swathe on our three-mile journey to Grand Central that I arrived at the station looking like I had just taken a shower and smelling like I needed one. Wimsey, however, was invigorated. He burst through the doors of Grand Central in full cry, gratified that his entourage had been expanded to include a bevy of camera-toting humans, all of whom seemed to be delightfully focused entirely upon him.

And the cameras weren't the only things focused entirely on him. If a baying bloodhound is difficult to ignore and a baying bloodhound in the middle of Grand Central Station is even more difficult to ignore, then a baying bloodhound in the middle of Grand Central Station accompanied by a photographer and a TV crew is a circus. And one in which Wimsey had appointed himself ringmaster. He was quickly surrounded by a large circle of onlookers bursting with admiration for his ability not to sit, not to stay and not to look at Jay's camera. Periodically he took breaks from these arduous activities to greet his public and allow them to scratch his ears.

It was during one of these breaks that Morry approached me.

"We're getting some great footage of him with the crowds. Now I'd like to get a closeup with him. Can I have his leash?"

I rapidly assessed the status of Morry's musculature. He was not a large man.

I could already see the headlines: *"CBS Correspondent in Hospital: Dragged By Giant Hound!"* Or worse, *"Multiple Casualties in Bloodhound Dragging Incident!"*

I tried to decide whether my best course of action would be to hover just outside camera range ready to pounce at the first sign of trouble or to position myself behind the camera and wave turkey in the hopes that Wimsey might condescend to look in its direction. I opted to hover. I also pulled the crew aside, briefed them on what Wimsey was likely to do and gave them instructions on how to effect Wimsey's recapture should he manage to slip past me.

When I was satisfied that everyone understood the gravity of the situation, I divested Wimsey's face of drool one last time and wrapped his leash tightly around Morry's outstretched hand.

"Hang onto him, he's kind of strong," I said with criminal understatement.

I sidled slowly away. I could feel the rivulets of sweat making channels in my makeup.

The channels got worse quickly. Morry unwound Wimsey's leash and held it lightly between his thumb and forefinger. Then he dropped to one knee and addressed the camera. I panicked. As far as Wimsey was concerned, low-lying humans could only mean one thing. Wrestling! It was sport in which he excelled and one in which he would find even less impediment since I saw that Morry had now dropped his leash entirely.

I was just debating whether it would be better to throw myself on top of Wimsey's head or to tackle his hindquarters when a strange thing happened. Nothing. Not only did Wimsey not decide to shoot off on some Excellent Grand Central Olfactory Adventure, but he also declined to wrestle Morry. Or climb on Morry. Or bay in Morry's face. Or fling drool on Morry. Or investigate Morry's private parts. In an astonishing display of canine rectitude Wimsey just stood there, calmly and quietly. And looking steadily straight into the camera.

The crew began to give me funny looks.

When it was over, the sound guy took me aside.

"See, he did great. You shouldn't worry so much. You just need to relax."

In spite of myself I was impressed. I had clearly underestimated Wimsey's ability to come up with a new and imaginative way to make me look like an idiot. It was of no use pointing out to the sound guy that if I had relaxed, Morry would have ended up bruised, battered and lying on the ground with clothing that looked like Swiss cheese.

Following his maiden excursion into the land of the well-behaved, Wimsey had a lot of making up to do and proceeded to do it in the CBS van on our way to Madison Square Garden. He made a colossal nuisance of himself climbing on everyone, snuffling everyone's clothing and faces and trying to snack on everyone's equipment. He licked the driver's ear. The crew loved him.

By the time we got to Madison Square Garden Wimsey was back in form. My plan was for Jay to photograph him with the digital sign advertising the Westminster Kennel Club Dog Show in the background. Fortunately for Wimsey, the sign was on a lengthy digital loop so he had more than enough time between the ad's appearance to try to trip pedestrians and to lift his leg in places where his efforts were unlikely to be appreciated. Whenever Jay's camera rudely interrupted these important activities, he displayed his nostrils, his profile or did his vulture imitation. Or he simply got up and left.

After his operatic triumph in Grand Central, Wimsey was clearly annoyed with this new assignment and he had a very special way of letting me know. Wimsey was unneutered and you didn't have to be around him very long before you realized that he used one of his organs like humans used a mood ring. Jay was kept busy photoshopping out the exuberant splashes of pink that habitually made their unwanted appearances between his legs. But if Wimsey was really annoyed he kept it safely tucked away. The Westminster sign really annoyed him.

But If Wimsey's extravagant displays of his organ weren't quite the thing for a children's book, in real life his reproductive equipment was a veritable tour de force of children's sex education. Whether it was his generously proportioned and fascinating set of testicles, ("Mommy what are those things swinging between his legs?") or the joyful appearance of his penis ("Mommy, what's that pink thing sticking out?"), Wimsey was more than happy to supply New York City parents with an abundance of teachable moments whether they wanted them or not. Such was the case one day when Wimsey and I swung around the corner of West 73rd Street, a narrow, residential thoroughfare with splendid acoustics. A little boy and his mother approached us from behind.

"Mommy! Mommy!" the little guy screamed at the top of his small but surprisingly powerful lungs, "That dog is a boy because I can see his penis!" Clearly confident in his subject and in no mood to be denied his moment to shine, he began to shout, "I can see his penis! I can see his penis! I can see his penis!" like a town crier calling for the urgent defense of the realm. This being New York City, his efforts attracted a not inconsiderable amount of attention.

Who's penis? Where is this penis? Should we call the police about this penis? Is there a flasher on the street?

There was. Wimsey enjoyed his walk.

CHAPTER 8--WIMSEY AT WESTMINSTER

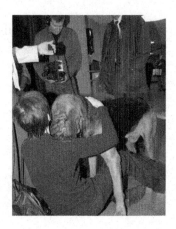

Fortunately, Maria's on camera interview went better than my off camera handling and the CBS segment about Wimsey aired multiple times during the weekend before Westminster. Every time Wimsey went out for a walk people kept stopping us to ask if he was the dog from TV. It was gratifying to be holding the leash of a dog who for once was famous rather than infamous and it was at least some measure of compensation for his persistent attempts to kill us on the stairs or to inflict damage with his many weaponized body parts.

Westminster Monday began at an unsociably early hour and found us all huddled excitedly in our Pet

Chauffeur taxi as we sped through the cold and quiet streets of Manhattan to Madison Square Garden. Realistically, Maria and I had no expectation that Wimsey would win any ribbons given the high level of competition and his lack of ranking points. But that didn't stop us from thinking "what if" as we gazed at Wimsey. His rich mahogany-colored coat gleamed, his sharply delineated black saddle was glossy and his deep-flewed face-- now making drool tracks on the windows--was undeniably expressive.

The car dropped us at the side entrance to the Garden and we joined a snaking conga line of canines waiting to have their credentials checked for entry. It was a madhouse. There were dogs everywhere and of every description. Some were in crates being towed on carts and some, like Wimsey, were on a leash, and all were accompanied by heavily burdened humans toting the extensive paraphernalia that is part and parcel of show doggery. And it was loud. Barks, yips, howls, woos and the occasional bay sliced through the frosty air as we slowly advanced towards the loading area.

Once our credentials passed muster, we proceeded to a large service elevator. As we joined the packed crowd inside I suddenly realized that Wimsey was being uncharacteristically quiet. It was unclear whether this was due to the unusual density of people and dogs or to all the chaotic shouting and noise. Wimsey could be a knucklehead, but he was a sensitive knucklehead. And at the moment he was not a happy knucklehead. His tail was threatening to tuck, he was panting and I could sense that he was giving serious consideration to trying to make a run for it at the earliest opportunity. I tightened my grip on his leash.

When the elevator door opened it disgorged us into a cold windswept, concrete passage. Wimsey looked around dubiously as we progressed up this passageway to look for the area dedicated to multi-breed handlers where Diane was located. The area was a huge disappointment. It was cold, noisy and far away from the general benching area where Maria and I had been looking forward to talking to the public about Wimsey. Basking in Wimsey's reflected glory was one of the very few perks associated with being around him. If you ever want to know what it feels like to be a celebrity, try walking a bloodhound on the streets of New York.

We established Wimsey in a warm and heavily padded crate--he was probably the only one of us who was warm--and went to take a look at the other bloodhounds. If this had been a movie Wimsey would have been the best of the bunch. But it wasn't and he wasn't. And while Wimsey was not exactly in tube sock territory, even to our untutored eyes, he had an unfinished look compared to the other hounds.

"I never thought I would say this, but Wimsey almost kind of looks smooth," Maria observed.

"Yeah, I don't think there will be any ribbons for him today," I sighed.

But if ribbons weren't going to materialize, a media entourage quickly did. As ring time approached, Jay arrived and was joined by some of the recipients of my press releases and also by our old friends from CBS who wanted to be on hand in the unlikely event of an upset. Maria, meanwhile, banished herself into the stands so as not to distract Wimsey (although I'm pretty sure he knew exactly where she was given that no one could eat a pizza anywhere on the Upper West Side without him knowing about it) and when he entered the arena he entered it trailed by a phalanx of photographers, reporters and TV cameras. The attention did not go unnoticed.

Maria happened to be sitting next to two women whose bloodhounds were also being shown.

"Why are they paying so much attention to that dog. Who even is he?" said one to the other. Then they tore him apart like a couple of characters from *Best in Show*. The ladies needn't have wasted their breath.

Maria and I had both assumed that whatever Wimsey's physical defects they might at least be partially offset by a display of stellar showmanship. If city streets were anything to go by, Wimsey would command the ring like he owned it. But the Wimsey that we knew and frequently wanted to kill, the energetic, charismatic and deeply obnoxious hound who had so often brought us to our knees, both literally and figuratively, had vanished. In his place there appeared a dog so shy and quiet that he wasn't even remotely recognizable as the baying ringmaster of The Grand Central Station Circus.

"What's the matter with Wimsey," Jay asked. "Is he sick?"

"I don't know. He was fine this morning," I replied. "But I've never seen him like this."

Wimsey didn't even come close to placing in the order of finish, but no sooner had he set paw outside of the ring than things turned around with a vengeance.

"Wimsey!" Maria shouted, as she knelt down on the ground and flung her arms out wide.

Wimsey, now relieved of the dispiriting exigencies of the show ring, liberated himself from his handler and barreled into her with the force worthy of a Super Bowl ring. Then he stood on top of her, dug his talons deep into her internal organs and smeared the contents of his drool-filled flews all over her face. It was an activity he interrupted only to issue loud bays of triumph.

The cameras clicked and the video rolled.

Wimsey was back! And he was now "showing" everywhere except where we had wanted him to. He made gregarious incursions into the crowds during his trips to the potty areas and when not behaving like a mayor running for re-election, he jammed his nose into people's backsides making them jump and squeal in a manner he found profoundly satisfying. And his loud baying attracted so much attention that it felt like everyone with a ticket was fighting their way forward to meet him. On every side we heard "Oh my god! He's gorgeous! Did he win?!" He certainly acted like he had. In between amusing himself in the potty area by trying to pee through its chain link fence onto people's legs, he exuded championship like a heady perfume.

We found his demeanor in the ring profoundly puzzling but we had little time to ruminate since Wimsey was in heavy demand for interviews throughout the day. The *Best in Show* ladies would have been incensed, especially when we were approached by an official looking gentleman.

"I'm from the Westminster Kennel Club Communications Department," he said. "Is Wimsey available to do interviews upstairs at 2pm?"

"He'd be delighted to," Maria replied, believing that "Oh hell yes" lacked a certain dignity. The man handed her a media appointment card and disappeared into the crowd.

A little before two, we leashed Wimsey up and made our way through the crowds to the exit. A guard blocked our way. We showed him our appointment card.

"No dog leaves the floor," he announced.

"Well he's supposed to do interviews upstairs," I replied. "What should we do?"

"You have to go to the Steward's Desk," he said and pointed. The Steward's Desk was at the opposite end of the packed benching area.

"Well this is going to be fun," I observed to Maria. It wasn't. At least not for us. Trying to maneuver a large, powerful and excited bloodhound through a dense wall of human and canine flesh was a horror show. Wimsey enjoyed it immensely. It was even better than going for a potty break. We arrived at the Steward's Desk, no thanks to Wimsey, and explained our predicament to the Steward. He looked at our appointment card and handed us a different document. I shortened Wimsey's leash and back we went. I handed the paper to the guard, trying to keep Wimsey's nose off of his uniform.

"Nope," he announced. "He can't leave." Trip number three across the floor was just as enjoyable as trips one and two. We again spoke to the Steward. The Steward handed us an additional piece of paper. We returned to the guard.

"He still can't leave," he said as he perused the paper. While it was reassuring to know that the Westminster Kennel Club took security seriously, this was starting to feel a bit excessive. The only one who didn't think so was Wimsey. He had turned himself around and was baying, no doubt eager to see his old friend the Steward again and to make new friends along the way. This time even the Steward was frustrated. He picked up a phone and spoke into it.

"Wait here," he said. Five minutes later the crowd parted and David Frei himself, Westminster's celebrity Director of Communications appeared. Wimsey swished his tail enthusiastically. He loved having a new human added to his entourage especially an important one. The combination of David Frei plus a baying bloodhound was a showstopper. Everyone came forward. Wimsey basked.

"They're with me," our escort briskly informed the guard even before he has a chance to open his mouth. Fort Knox has nothing on the Westminster Kennel Club Dog Show.

Things went downhill from there. We were ushered into a large room with tables, chairs, sofas and bookcases, all of which Wimsey wished to inspect and all which I didn't want him to. We had to conduct the interviews at a shout. I have no idea how long we were there except that it was too long. I was hoarse and my arms ached with the effort of trying to keep Wimsey's explorations to a minimum. Even the cold, windy passage was starting to look good. By the time we finished trying to convince the last reporter that the irate, baying dog I was struggling to keep at my side was going to star in a book for children, I was more than ready to make our escape. I just hoped that getting back onto the floor was easier than getting off of it.

But as soon as we left the interview room an arty looking guy appeared from down the hall.

"Great looking dog," he commented. "We'd like to take pictures of him for next year's publicity campaign." He obviously hadn't heard any of Wimsey's interviews.

"Sure," I found myself saying for reasons I can't explain. Maria was mouthing the words "Are you insane?" The man ushered us into the photography studio. It was a bright, white room with lights, equipment and people all arranged around a raised platform.

"Could you take off his leash and have him sit on the platform please," the photographer said. He might just as well have asked Wimsey to perform The Dance of the Sugar Plum Fairy. Wimsey did not wish to sit on the platform. He didn't wish to sit anywhere. He wished to investigate all the new and interesting things that he was not supposed to investigate. He alternated between poking his nose where it wasn't wanted and trying to wipe his face on people's pants. Every so often he went over to the door to check if it was still shut. In between all of this, Maria and I herded him onto the platform. It was probably only due to sheer negligence on Wimsey's part that there were any photographs taken of him at all.

Fortunately the rest of our Westminster experience was uneventful. Wimsey napped, we froze. It was still an improvement.

Westminster is a benched show and all the dogs had to remain at their assigned places until 7pm. But since carefully checking the exit credentials of several thousand dogs is not a rapid process, it wasn't until 10 pm that I finally made it back to my apartment. My first act was to reach for the aspirin and the gin, not necessarily in that order.

Seven blocks away, Wimsey also made it home after 10pm and his first act was to reach for Maria's dinner and her bed in precisely that order.

Wimsey had had a wonderful time. At least somebody had.

CHAPTER 9--AN INTERNATIONAL HOUND

The next day, Maria and I scoured the papers like actors after opening night. Some papers had pictures of Wimsey while others just mentioned him. Now we were stopped by even more people on the street excited to know if Wimsey was the dog from Westminster. New Yorkers love a celebrity even if it has four legs and a tail and flings drool in their face.

But it was soon back to work on the book and the next shoot on my list was The United Nations. I hadn't been there since I was a teenager when a friend and I made the useful discovery that since the UN is international territory its restaurant isn't bound by New York State's drinking age laws. Our parents were delighted that their daughters took such a keen interest in international diplomacy.

Wimsey, too, seemed to take a keen interest in international diplomacy if the speed with which he towed me the three and half miles to its epicenter was anything to go by. The reason for his enthusiasm became apparent as soon as we arrived. Tourist sniffing was one of Wimsey's principal hobbies and the UN appeared to be especially well stocked with them. And although Wimsey found all non-local scents intoxicating the ones that originated overseas were even more so. Fortunately his interest seemed to be reciprocated and as soon as we arrived he was enveloped by an eager throng discussing him in the languages of many lands.

While Wimsey busily applied his nose to his new friends like a sommelier with a fine Bordeaux, I began to prepare the prop for today's shoot. I had found a globe-colored beach ball on Amazon and I wanted Wimsey to play with it with the iconic General Assembly Building looming in the background. I thought Wimsey would find the idea especially to his liking since he had been a great lover of all things spherical since puppyhood. One of his favorite games was to find an abandoned tennis or lacrosse ball, whack it with his paw and then chase it up and down the lawns of Central Park like a midfielder in the World Cup. When he was done he would tuck it into a handy flew and carry it home to add to his mud-encrusted collection on Maria's carpet.

Based on all available data I was certain the beachball was going to be a huge hit.

"Look Wimsey! A ball!" I called out when I had finished inflating it. Wimsey tore himself away from his snuffle diplomacy to have a look. He sniffed the ball, poked it briefly with his nose and then turned around and went back the way he came.

"I thought you said he liked balls," Jay said. "Is there a Plan B?"

"This is Wimsey. I always have a Plan B."

I removed a tub of cream cheese from my backpack. Wimsey materialized like he had been teleported. He didn't even wait for me to smear the cream cheese on the ball before he started baying at me. When I was finished, I placed the cream cheesed ball on the ground and crossed my fingers that it wouldn't suffer the same fate as Balto. It didn't. Wimsey was happy to lick the cream cheese off the ball. What he wasn't happy to do was play with it.

I took the ball away and tossed it high in the air, thinking that the movement might cause him to reconsider. Wimsey watched the ball go up. He watched the ball go down. He watched the ball roll away. Then he bayed at me because he wanted more cream cheese. When none was forthcoming he returned to his friends ready to greet any new arrivals like a host at a cocktail party.

"Is there a Plan C?" Jay asked.

"No, but if he won't play with the ball maybe I can get him to rest his paw on it like he owns the world."

"Well he certainly seems to. Anyway, see if you can get him to do it over here. There's a good view of the General Assembly Building."

I reeled Wimsey to the spot Jay indicated, placed his paw on top of the ball and darted out of frame. Wimsey removed his paw from the ball and also darted out of frame.

The international peanut gallery thought this was hilarious.

I retrieved Wimsey and this time I held his paw on top of the ball with one hand and fed him turkey with the other. Who knows? Maybe a light bulb would go off in his pointy head and he'd realize that the way to get more turkey was to keep his paw on the ball. Or not. Every time I removed the turkey, Wimsey removed his paw.

"Don't do it! Don't do it!" the crowd began to chant at every attempt. Schadenfreude was alive and well at the UN that day.

Wimsey's cheerleaders also posed an additional problem. They were all congregated stage right and their wafting scent acted like a crank to move Wimsey's head in that direction.

"Can you get him to keep his head straight," Jay called out. I took out some turkey and lured Wimsey's head straight.

"Well his head is straight but he's got his eyes rolled all the way to right," Jay informed me. I looked at the picture. I could see the whites of Wimsey's eyes. He looked like an inmate of a canine insane asylum.

I stood behind Jay, waved turkey and made high-pitched squealy noises. Wimsey looked at me. Then he took his paw off the ball.

"Plan D?" Jay inquired.

"Nope. I give up. We'll just have to come back when I figure something else out."

While I packed up--much to the disappointment of his fans--Jay began to idly photograph Wimsey doing this and that. An Asian gentleman wandered over to inspect

Wimsey at closer range. Wimsey, who happened to be standing near the ball, turned his head to return the favor. It looked like they were discussing some important international issue, like perhaps increasing the importation of Squeaky Teddy's relatives or reducing tariffs on animal parts.

We had our photo.

But the day was far from over. I still needed to get Wimsey home. Wimsey liked this side of town and the enthusiasm with which he had dragged me to the East Side was now matched by his reluctance to leave it. Its toney residents were, if anything, even more effusive with respect to his beauty, his rarity and his show dog status than those of the more plebian West. Not that the West Side didn't have its moments. Like when a svelte young man attired in elegant black pointed to Wimsey and declared to his friends, "Now THAT is fashion," in a rich European accent. The fact that Fashion was at that moment happily shedding his black and tan label all over everyone's couture didn't seem to bother him at all.

It was several hours and much turkey later when I had finally persuaded Wimsey as far as Park Avenue. We were standing in the median that divides it waiting for the light to change when I saw a familiar face crossing in the opposite direction. It was Joan Rivers, impeccably dressed and tottering precariously on a pair of lofty stilettos. She stared at Wimsey. Wimsey stared at her. I also stared at her, unsure of which was more alarming--the danger Wimsey posed to her clothes or her to balance. Of the many things that I foresaw could possibly go wrong that day, Wimsey flinging drool onto Joan Rivers or sending her to the hospital was not among them. Nor was causing her to get run over. She stopped abruptly in the middle of traffic, and pointed a long, manicured finger at Wimsey.

"Fabulous! Fabulous! "Fabulous!" she proclaimed in her raspy voice while using her manicured finger to emphasize Wimsey's fabulosity. Amazingly, the traffic flowed harmlessly around her.

I, on the other hand was completely non-fabulous. My ancient, mud-encrusted, drool-stained parka hailed from the fashion house of LL Bean and I was wearing a pair of baggy and highly unflattering jeans which displayed evidence of recent contact with both Wimsey's mouth and his paws. My footwear consisted of a pair of battered New Balance (badly misnamed) running shoes and I had an enormous black leather fanny pack slung around my waist. My coiffure--courtesy of Wimsey--consisted of hair plastered to my head with a mixture of dried sweat and drool. I also exuded a powerful and pungent aroma of hound that swirled around me like a dust storm.

If Joan Rivers had actually been the Fashion Police, I would have been arrested.

CHAPTER 10--A MODEL CANINE

In the months following Westminster, Wimsey's popularity continued unabated and it gave me a new idea.

"What do you think about Wimsey modeling?" I asked Maria, conveniently ignoring the fact that although the camera loved Wimsey the reverse could not be said to be true.

"That's a great idea!" she replied, also conveniently ignoring this fact.

I researched New York's animal talent agencies and my inbox was soon filled with a gratifying number of invitations to submit Wimsey's credentials. I guessed that they weren't over supplied with bloodhounds. I couldn't imagine why.

The applications were all pretty similar and their first parts were easy—they needed pictures of Wimsey and information about his height, weight, breed and age. The next section was Wimsey's bio in which I made sure to mention that he was a show dog. But the third section had me stumped. I had to list Wimsey's Special Skills and Talents. What could those be? Baying? Or wrestling? Long distance drool flinging? Or perhaps canine martial arts; Wimsey could do more damage with his body parts than a pair of nunchuk sticks. I left it blank. Not that Wimsey would actually do any of these things, or anything else, on command but I had convinced myself that in a quiet studio with a minimum of distractions, he would do fine.

A couple of months later I called Maria with the exciting news that Wimsey had booked his first gig.

"What's it for?" was her first question. "And what does he have to do?" was her second. She had spent far too many hours listening to my accounts of Wimsey's photoshoots.

"The agency said they don't have any information yet. The only thing they know is that the shoot is way out on Long Island and that the owner of the agency is going to drive us out there."

Being completely in the dark as to what Wimsey would have to do was so unsettling that I prepared for his modeling debut like a five-star general planning an assault on an intractable foe. I had a mini mountain of spit rags, toys, bones and chewies, a variety of harnesses, a slip chain and the heinous Gentle Leader and its evil cousin, The Halti. And instead of turkey, I had what I thought would be ne plus ultra of Wimsey bribing snacks—a large bag of smelly sliced hotdogs.

I was as ready as I would ever be bright and early one beautiful summer's morning when Wimsey and I waited in front of Maria's building. A large SUV soon rolled up and a stocky, gray-haired gentleman got out and introduced himself. His arrival threw Wimsey into loud paroxysms of joy. He wanted everyone in the neighborhood to know that he was about to embark on a car trip and as soon as the man opened the rear door Wimsey flung himself inside like he was afraid it would escape without him. Wimsey was as passionate about cars as he was about balls and anyone who failed to step lively when entering or exiting a car or taxi ran the serious risk of having a large and enthusiastic guest.

"Do you know what the assignment is?" I asked as soon as it was quiet enough to make myself heard.

"Yes, it's a catalog shoot for J. Crew," he replied. This seemed innocuous enough and although I obviously knew it would be a bit of a challenge to stop Wimsey from drooling on the clothing, it rang no alarm bells. But then he followed it up with a question.

"Does Wimsey like other dogs?" he asked. It struck me as a bit late to be asking this question but Wimsey's bio did say he was a show dog and being a show dog is like going to Harvard—people made assumptions. In Wimsey's case it wasn't about intelligence but about behavior. Being a show dog meant that Wimsey was obedient, well-behaved and liked other dogs. Although one out of three was correct, liking other dogs was perhaps understating the case a bit. If wildly baying, pouncing, wrestling, chasing and exhibiting an insatiable desire to stick one's nose up everyone's backside was liking other dogs, then, yes, Wimsey liked other dogs. But Wimsey's social activities also led to the production of lengthy ropes of drool which he was happy to share with everything around him. Which in this case would be cameras, equipment and ladies trying to model clothing. I was horrified.

"Don't worry," the man said, mistaking the reason for the look on my face, "most of the other dogs are show dogs also."

During the next several hours, when not contemplating the grim prospects of my immediate future, the agent told me how he started the agency after learning how to train dogs in the military. Since military dog trainers generally use dominance-oriented methods not much in favor these days, I tactfully omitted any discussion of training philosophy when I chatted with him about my work at the ASPCA and my success in training large and powerful breeds. I conveniently omitted the fact that none of these successes involved Wimsey.

When we at last left the highway we bounced down leafy country lanes until we finally pulled onto a large property where Mother Nature could be said to have gotten the upper hand. The buildings were of the derelict, haunted mansion variety and I half expected to see Morticia Addams pop out of a doorway. But there was nothing derelict about all the activity--people, lights, trailers, cameras and of course, dogs, littered the landscape. The latter seemed to range in size from a stately Great Dane to a diminutive Jack Russell. It looked like Wimsey's idea of heaven and mine of some place considerably further to the south.

Since the agent said that we weren't needed immediately I decided to walk Wimsey around the property. I told him that I wanted to acclimate Wimsey to the surroundings. What I really wanted to do was to work on his less than reliable sit-stays.

As soon as we were a discrete distance away, I asked Wimsey to sit. As usual, he took it under advisement. After weighing the pros and cons, he finally decided that he had nothing better to do. He sat. I triumphantly produced a piece of hot dog. Wimsey regarded the hot dog with suspicion. He twitched his nose at it. He extended a tentative tongue and gave it a lick. Then deciding that it had a high probability of being edible, he cautiously removed it from my fingers like he thought it might bite him. He masticated the hot dog in a slow and judicial way and when he finally swallowed it he concluded that it was not an experience he cared to repeat. He walked away to pee on a bush.

I was stunned. And while I ruminated on the implications of my miscalculation—I had neglected to bring an alternative--I heard the director call for the Jack Russell. I saw the little dog hop out of its car. Wimsey immediately lifted his snout and flared his nostrils to such an extent that I feared for the integrity of his nose. Then he emitted a series of bays so thunderous that the vibration hurt my ears. People stared. Some laughed.

I was grateful that catalog shoots didn't have microphones. A few of weeks ago, Wimsey and I had been zipping along the bridle path in Central Park when he came to an abrupt halt next to a crowd watching a movie shoot. Wimsey wished to sniff the crowd watching the movie shoot. I wished him not to. He and I were sharing our views on the matter when a ruckus erupted from somewhere deep inside the crowd.

"Cut!" someone screamed. A large, red-faced man charged out of the crowd. "Get that f------ thing the f--- off my set," he yelled, his face growing redder by the second.

It wasn't every dog whose resumé included getting kicked out of Central Park.

But even in the absence of microphones, I thought it would be a good idea to get Wimsey as far away from the Jack Russell as possible. Wimsey didn't like this decision any more than he liked the one in Central Park. He sounded like Chewbacca on the loose. And regardless of which way I tugged his body, his head (and voice) remained firmly pointed towards the Jack Russell. Even taking into account Wimsey's exceptionally gregarious nature, I had never seen him so fixated on one particular dog before. But the tone of his baying wasn't aggressive so I assumed that he just really, really wanted to play with it.

Then the owner of the agency stomped over. He was not pleased.

"He's unsettling all the other dogs. Make him stop," he ordered.

King Canute had better odds. I dragged a protesting Wimsey even further away and prayed for some exciting development like a racoon or a herd of fast moving rodents to distract him. My efforts using toys, rawhides, bones and hot dogs certainly weren't. It did briefly cross my mind that there might be another explanation for Wimsey's odd behavior and I took it up with the agent when he returned to yell at me some more.

"Is the Jack Russel by any chance female?" I asked. "And is it possible that she's coming into heat?"

"No," he replied, "she's just finished her heat."

"Why did someone bring a dog this close to heat to a shoot with male dogs?" I asked him. He immediately became defensive.

"None of the other male dogs are behaving like this. Only him." The agent continued, rounding on the offensive, "He's a show dog. He's around intact female dogs all the time. He shouldn't behave this!"

But he was behaving like this. Wimsey was young. He was male. And he had the bloodhound's exquisite sense of smell. It was like asking a sixteen-year-old boy to sit in a room with a naked woman and read Proust. It wasn't often—in fact never—that I was on Wimsey's side, but this time, improbably I was. I kept my thoughts to myself, however, and apologized.

I really didn't think this day could get any worse. But then the agent reappeared holding something in his hand.

"The director wants the models to line up holding the dogs." He pointed to Wimsey's slip chain. "He can't wear that, put him in this," he said, and handed me an ordinary buckle collar. The situation as I saw it, was now as follows: Wimsey would be attached to a slender model who might quite possibly be wearing heels. There would be dogs to the right of him, dogs to the left of him and one of them would be in heat. And he would be wearing a buckle collar. The day definitely got worse. Much worse.

I walked over to the line of models and sidled up as close as possible to Wimsey's victim before I swapped out his collar.

"Hang onto him, he's strong," I said, hoping that that the model didn't notice my lack of confidence in her ability to do so. I stuffed a piece of hot dog into Wimsey's reluctant mouth, waved another in front of his nose and slowly backed up with my hand in the "stay" position, all for purely theatrical purposes.

Wimsey was about as interested in staying as he was in eating hot dogs. He promptly shoved his nose into both his neighbors' backsides and then loudly proclaimed his availability for activities of a more spirited nature. The line dissolved in pandemonium. The handlers moved in to restore order and I repeated my pantomime with the hot dog. Wimsey ignored it in favor of trying to introduce himself to the large Great Dane standing at the head of the line. As he began to drag his stumbling model in its direction, it was clear that something drastic had to be done. I pulled out Squeaky Teddy. I gave Squeaky Teddy a loud squeak. The line went insane.

The agent, some serious steam coming out of his ears, marched over and suggested that he take charge. It was pretty obvious that he thought I was the problem. I was a weak and unassertive female handler trying to control a dog who needed the firm hand of an authoritative and dominant male. I decided not to enlighten him as to his error. I might even have smiled as I handed over Wimsey's leash. Wimsey was a large and powerful dog so muscling him around wasn't going to hurt him. It was also not going to work.

I watched as the agent seized Wimsey's leash in a forceful manner and administered a series of sharp leash corrections. Then, as I had predicted, he pushed Wimsey around, walked into his space, issued instructions in a low and commanding voice and assumed a dominant physical posture.

When he felt that he had made his point, he gave Wimsey one last growl and handed his leash to the model. He was sweating. Wimsey decided to take off in the direction of the Jack Russell. Another rumpus ensued. The photographer called it quits.

During lunch, the agent, now even more annoyed, approached me. It was Wimsey's special genius to make even the most experienced dog trainer look like an incompetent neophyte. I should know.

"Your dog doesn't work for food, he doesn't work to please you (a vast understatement if only he knew) and he doesn't intimidate. How do you get him to do what you want?"

"If I knew that, I'd have my own TV show," I replied.

It was an excruciatingly long and loud day most of which was spent trying to keep Wimsey entertained, out of trouble and off of the Jack Russell with only limited success. The ride home was understandably tense. The only one who enjoyed it was Wimsey. He alternated between looking out of the window, snoring loudly and farting copiously. From his point of view he had had a very successful day—he had made new friends, smelled new smells and had been the focus of everyone's attention.

When we finally got home, I deposited Wimsey on his couch, updated Maria on how much I hated her dog and then slunk home to consume several aspirin and a large quantity of gin. Wimsey really should have been modeling for Bayer and Tanqueray.

Several weeks later, when I received a check from the agency, it was for only half the amount of the fee. That was because the agency had received only half of its fee on account of Wimsey.

"That's my boy," Maria commented when I told her. Needless to say, I never expected to hear from these people again.

CHAPTER 11--THE HOUSEGUEST FROM HELL

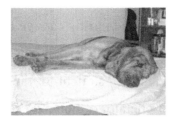

Up until this point my experience of Wimsey had been acquired largely at the end of his leash. All that changed the day Maria called to ask if Wimsey could stay with me over Thanksgiving.

"Of course he can," I exclaimed. "It's a great idea. It will give me a chance to work on his training." I was incredibly excited. Not only did I think it would be fun to have Wimsey full time for a few days but I also believed it might strengthen our bond and maybe even make me important enough for him to listen to. I completely ignored the fact that he lived with Maria and didn't listen to her either.

On Wednesday afternoon I met Maria, Wimsey and all Wimsey's stuff outside my building. Unlike Maria whose building was a small walkup, mine was large and busy and had a doorman, a concierge and elevator operators. Wimsey was immediately taken with the idea of meeting all these new and mostly captive friends. He charged into the lobby like he owned it, hung a left at the concierge desk and headed straight for the quaking, uniformed elevator operator. I thought the man was going to pass out.

"Don't worry," I called out, "he just wants to say hello." My assurances fell on deaf ears. It didn't help that Wimsey was baying and straining at the end of his leash at the time and when we piled into the elevator its operator was pressed so tightly against its side that it looked like he was trying to merge with it.

But the elevator and its operator were but one of the many attractions of my building. When the elevator door opened it revealed Teddy, my neighbor's shy little mini-goldendoodle. Wimsey tried to introduce himself to Teddy in much the same way as he had tried to introduce himself to the elevator operator. It was the second time I had to apologize in less than a minute. We were off to a great start.

I hauled Wimsey down the hall and shoved him into my apartment and while we began to unpack his belongings he began to inspect mine. He busied himself like a museum curator with an exceptionally fine trove.

Maria set up his elevated feeding and watering station.

"Wimsey is a finicky eater," she reminded me, although given the hot dog episode it was hardly something I was likely to forget, "so just make sure he always has kibble. He eats whenever he gets hungry."

As soon as the kibble hit the bowl Wimsey arrived to investigate. He sniffed the kibble dismissively and plunged his snout into his water bowl instead. When he lifted his face there was a messy waterfall cascading off of it. He gave one brisk shake of the head and it all went flying onto the walls, ceilings, floors and me.

"I wouldn't stand too close to him when he's drinking," Maria advised seeing the goo dripping from my face. "But have fun!" she added and kissed Wimsey and headed out the door. Wimsey ignored her departure and went to wipe the remaining moisture from his face along the side of the couch.

I work from home, so after cleaning up the kitchen I sat down at my desk to resume work. While I occupied myself with my project Wimsey occupied himself with his. This consisted of him rooting around in the recyclables pile in the kitchen and then transferring selected items to the Oriental rug so he could shred them. When he had completed the work to his satisfaction he napped on top of the remains.

Several hours later I heard the sound of ear flapping. A piece of an oatmeal box hit me in the head. Then suddenly instead of my keyboard I found myself typing on Wimsey's head. When I pushed it aside and pulled the keyboard return back out, he dove under the desk and into its nest of wires. The computer went dark. Work was over for the day.

Thinking that I would catch up on the papers, I settled myself on the couch. I could hear Wimsey having a drink. But this time there was no sound of ear flapping. That was because he was standing in front of me with his dripping flews. Before the words, "Wimsey no!" were out of my mouth I was once again covered in water and slime. I wiped my face with a tissue. Wimsey wiped his face with my pants. Then he stood back and stared at me with his tail swishing to and fro. I was just wondering what this meant when he climbed into my lap and made himself comfortable on top of the newspapers I had been trying to read. Then he thwacked me with a paw to scratch him. Newspaper reading was also apparently over for the day.

This was not going at all as I had planned. Clearly I needed to exert a little more control over the situation and I thought that there was no better place to do so than on a walk. I tried to get up. I couldn't. Wimsey had me pinned to the couch.

"Wimsey off!" I commanded. Wimsey looked at me happily and thumped his tail We wrestled. I won. Although not without the uncomfortable feeling that he had let me.

My studio apartment has a little dressing room and I went into it to change into dog walking clothes with Wimsey in close attendance. He danced around and poked his cold nose into my exposed flesh to hurry me along. He seemed just as eager to go out for a walk as I was. I picked up his collar and leash. He backed away and stared at me. His head was slightly lowered and his front legs slightly splayed. He swished his tail. Then he took off like a rabbit. Around and around the circular layout of my apartment we went like figures on a merry-go-round. When I changed directions so did he. For such a large dog he was surprisingly agile. As I watched him parkour off the couch it occurred to me that not only was I never going to catch him but that my efforts to do so hardly constituted exerting control. I did what I should have done in the first place. I went over to the door and took a piece of turkey out of my treat pouch. Wimsey screeched to a halt in front of me. As soon as I put on his collar and leash he couldn't get out the door fast enough.

Wimsey's walks were generally lengthy undertakings and he was loud and unhappy about the fact that this one had only lasted two hours. Judging by the volume of his protests and the insistence with which he tried to drag me in the opposite direction to the one in which I wanted to go, the walk did little in the way of exerting control. But I still had another trick up my sleeve when we went upstairs. One of the ways in which I intended to make myself important to Wimsey was by cooking him delicious food. He watched me sauté chunks of stew beef for his dinner with a gratifying intensity. I mixed the beef thoroughly with the kibble, placed the bowl in his feeding station and waited for him to dive in.

It was like watching Louis XIV at a Grand Couvert. Rather than diving in, Wimsey approached the bowl with a ceremonial slowness and conducted a visual inspection of its contents. It seemed to meet with his approval so he began to twitch his nose carefully over the bowl and evaluate its aroma. This too proved acceptable to the royal nose, so he moved on to the matter of an audience. Just like the kings of France, whose table his ancestors had helped supply, Wimsey expected to be observed while he ate. Maria had told me about this, but I had forgotten. It was a relic of his puppy training when she stood by his food bowl, occasionally adding choice bits to it, to make sure he never became food aggressive. Wimsey so enjoyed the mealtime attention that it was a custom he insisted be retained whenever possible. He gazed up at me to make sure he had my full attention. Only then did he deign to lower his head and actually eat. Although I am not sure eating was the right word. It was more like excavating. He used his snout like a shovel to separate the meat from the kibble from which it had been so carefully mixed.

When Wimsey had completed his meat mining there was so much kibble strewn all over the kitchen floor that I had serious doubts as to whether any of it made it into his stomach. But some of it had definitely made it into his mouth. He had a post-prandial drink and when he shook pieces of it hit me in the face. There were also bits of it stuck to my pants which he once again decided to use as a napkin. Then he sprawled out in the middle of the kitchen for a nap that turned my own dinner preparations into a dangerous game of Twister.

Having survived both our dinners I sat down on the couch to watch some TV. I pressed the remote control but nothing happened. I was just about to check the batteries when I noticed that Wimsey was standing in a spot that blocked the signal. I got up, pushed him out of the way and returned to the couch. He returned the spot. I went to the refrigerator and got a piece of turkey. He followed me, ate the turkey and returned to the spot.

I texted Maria.

"Oh yeah," she replied. "I forgot to tell you. He knows how to block the remote control so you can't watch TV. He probably just wants you to scratch him." I digested the information that although Wimsey was ostensibly unable to learn how to hold a stick in his mouth he had somehow acquired an advanced knowledge of electronics. But when I looked up from my phone Wimsey was no longer standing on the spot. He was standing in front of the couch. His tail was swishing. Then he climbed into my lap, once again oblivious to the fact that he lacked the one essential quality of a lap dog. And although he was no longer blocking the remote, he was blocking everything else. The only thing I could see was fur. Then he thwacked me just in case I hadn't noticed that he was there and wanted to be scratched.

By the time 10:30 rolled around my neck was stiff with the effort of craning around him to watch TV. But it was time for his last walk of the night anyway. Maria had assured me it would be a quick, 30-minute potty-oriented affair.

Or a two-hour tour of the Upper West Side. We got home at 12:30. He had tried to drag me to Central Park.

As soon as I opened the door Wimsey shot through it and made a beeline for his feeding station to see if the Food Fairy had left him something more interesting than kibble while he had been away. Seeing that she hadn't he consoled himself with a drink while I stowed my outerwear and put away his walking equipment. It couldn't have taken me more than two minutes. But in this brief span Wimsey had somehow managed to finish his drink, fling drool on the kitchen walls, wipe his face on the couch--there was a fresh smear along the side--and ascend the futon which doubled as my bed at night. I found him there snoring in a highly improbable way.

I had no objection to Wimsey sleeping with me, in fact quite the contrary. Sleeping together was part of my bonding plan. But Maria had warned me that even as a little puppy, Wimsey refused to share the bed with her. But regardless of where he slept I still needed to change the sheets. The futon was currently made up with the set Maria had given me for Wimsey and they sported an unappetizing patina of hound hair, hound stink, dried drool and a number of other stains into whose origin I was not inclined to delve too deeply. But they were nonetheless incredibly soft. Wimsey insisted on this. During the day he slept on

Maria's bed and if she made it up with sheets of insufficient thread count he simply rucked them up and slept on the mattress instead.

Soft or not, they were not anything that I wanted to sleep on. I poked him.

"C'mon Wimsey, move. You can come back up afterwards."

The snoring continued. If there was an Oscar for playing possum, Wimsey would have been a leading contender. I scratched him. I played with his wrinkles. I massaged his dewlap. I looked into his ears. I grabbed his paw (which he firmly removed from my possession without missing a snorey beat). I tried to shove him off the bed but he pressed himself so deeply into it that he looked like a flounder. I finally grabbed the sheet at one end and used its leverage to try to roll him off. He glared at me and stepped off the bed with an annoyed snort. His absence was only temporary, however. While I was brushing my teeth I could hear sounds of the bedding being rearranged.

When I returned from the bathroom I found that he had repurposed my blanket as a pillow and was once again snoring in a very pointed fashion. I squeezed myself onto the only sliver of bed remaining. His head popped up. He gave me an angry stare, heaved a martyred sigh and left for somewhere less crowded. It was the highlight of the night.

Here's how it went:

1:30 am: Wimsey's snoring sounds like a motorcycle gang has invaded my apartment.

1:40 am: Earplugs don't work. I take an Ambien.

2:20 am: Am woken up by loud sounds of kibble crunching. Wimsey has apparently abandoned hope of the Food Fairy.

2:30 am: Crunching stops. Slurping starts.

2:35 am: Slurping stops. Ear flapping starts. I close my eyes and try not to think about the mess.

2:37 am: Wimsey, alarmed that I am not moving and therefore might possibly be dead, decides to test the hypothesis by snuffling my face with cold, wet wrinkles until I shriek. Thus reassured, he returns to the arms of Morpheus. I do not.

3 am: Am having a nightmare that I am in the trenches of World War I and can't breathe. Gas attack is real but caused by Wimsey not Germans. I get out of bed and open the window.

3:15 am: Wimsey has an extended scratch which he accompanies by loud, satisfied grunting.

3:40 am: Woken by sounds of ear flapping and digging coming from the Oriental rug.

5 am: Jolted awake. Wimsey is nibbling on my toes. Forgot that Maria warned me to always sleep with my hands and feet under the blanket.

7 am: I sense that I am being watched. I open my eyes. Wimsey's head is looming above mine. Seeing that I am awake he says good morning by blanketing my face with drooly wrinkles and pointy snout bristles.

I immediately catapult out of bed and into my clothes. Maria had assured me that Wimsey was not an early riser and that he much preferred sleeping in to doing anything distasteful like taking an early morning walk and relieving himself so she could get to work on time. I therefore concluded that my early wake-up call must mean that Wimsey had an urgent need to go out. But rather than anxiously waiting by the door as I had anticipated, Wimsey was comfortably tucked up in bed. His head was on my pillow and he was snoring contentedly. I rattled his leash and collar. He opened one eye and regarded me phlegmatically. Then he closed it again, this time more firmly. The snoring resumed. If I had a suspicious mind I would have noted that Wimsey was now in sole possession of the bed.

When I was finally able to bribe him out of bed and into his leash and collar, his initial reluctance to leave my apartment was exceeded only by his reluctance to go back in. Three and a half hours later, restored and invigorated by a brisk tow around the neighborhood, Wimsey consumed a hearty breakfast of scrambled eggs, turkey and kibble. Then he assisted me in the bath by using his tongue as a washcloth, shoving my bath products into the water, attempting to eat my pumice stone and occupying the bathmat in a way that threatened to turn me into a bathroom statistic. When I tried to do yoga he sat on me and drooled in my face.

It was a relief when Wimsey decided he had done enough for one morning and climbed onto the futon for a nap. I hoped it would be a long one. I was exhausted. I lay down on the couch and was immediately unconscious. At some point I became aware that my dream included a vaguely familiar slurping sound. I opened an eye just into time to get the contents of Wimsey's water bowl full in the face. Then he shoved his nose into one of my eyes sockets and completed the job with his tongue. With the unoccupied eye I could see his tail. It was swishing. I extended an arm to try to stop him, but he pushed it aside like an inconvenient twig and draped himself on top of me. The points of his joints dug painfully into sensitive parts of my anatomy. He seemed not to have gotten the memo that two objects could not occupy the same space at the same time. On the other hand, if he was on the couch, he wasn't on the futon and based on recent evidence, if I was on the futon, he wouldn't be. I wrestled myself out from under my unwelcome blanket and lay down on the futon. I was just starting to drift off when the bed creaked and I found Wimsey using my shoulder as a chin rest and breathing fish kibble fumes into my face.

I texted Maria. "Daytime naps don't count," came the reply.

That night, in spite of how tired I was I couldn't fall asleep. I lay there tensely expecting that any moment there would be another bed check. Or toe nibbling. Or ear flapping. Or kibble crunching and water slurping or being awakened by an alarm clock that had wet wrinkles and pointy bristles. When I did manage to fall asleep I hadn't been that way very long when I was awakened by the sound of loud clanging. I got up to investigate and found that Wimsey was in the throes of a dream so dynamic that it required him to kickbox my radiator. I padded the radiator with some blankets which muffled the clanging but did little to suppress the dream-related baying and the drum-like tail thumping that accompanied it.

But if nights with Wimsey were bad, days weren't much better. On his third day in residence I sat down at my desk hoping that he was too busy making a mess on my futon with his rawhide to bother me. Then I heard a thunk. I got up and saw that his bone had fallen off the bed. He was looking at it longingly. I picked it up and gave it back to him. He thumped his tail gratefully at me. I returned to my desk. There was another thunk. The bone was on the floor again. I replaced it and once again sat down. Another thunk. This time when I retrieved it I placed it in the middle of the bed, well away from the edge. I sat down. There were bed noises. Then a thunk. It finally dawned on me. The bone wasn't falling off the bed. Wimsey was throwing it off. He was teaching me to play fetch.

Five days of living with Wimsey felt like five weeks. I was counting the hours until he left. But although I was done with Wimsey, he wasn't done with me. Sunday morning I went out to run errands and when I returned Wimsey was not at the door as usual, ostensibly to greet me but really to nose wand me to see where I'd been or to poke his nose into my packages to see if there was anything he wanted. The reason he wasn't at the door was because he was on the windowsill. I saw with horror that all 120 pounds of him was perched with all four paws on its 7- inch width. I had no idea how it was possible for him to maintain his balance let alone how he had gotten up there. What I did know was that I had a knot the size of Manhattan in my stomach. If I startled him he might either fall off and break some important bone, like his neck, or else push through the window and fall onto the pavement fourteen floors below. Wimsey, however, seemed unconcerned by these possibilities. He glanced at me briefly and then returned to happily watching whatever riveting events were unfolding in Riverside Park across the street.

I crept up on him slowly and spoke softly to him. As soon as I was within reaching range I lunged for his dewlap and grabbed onto it with both hands like it was a life preserver. Wimsey didn't mind the dewlap grabbing but he definitely minded when I used it to maneuver him off the ledge and onto an adjacent table. He bayed at me and sent the table's contents flying across the room. I wondered whether it was too early for gin.

Several hours later, Maria called to say she was home. This was a good thing because if Wimsey didn't electrocute himself with computer wires or kill himself on windowsills I was going to do it for him.

"Come get your horrible hound! Now!" I yelled into the phone.

Four nights with no sleep will do that to you.

She chuckled. "Surely this can't be Wimsey you're talking about?"

After Maria picked Wimsey up I surveyed the damage. My walls, ceilings, windows, TV and computer looked like they had been decorated by Jackson Pollack, my yoga pants were now black and tan, there were stray bits of kibble on the floor, in the refrigerator and under my sheets, and my floors crunched when I walked from a combination of smashed kibble bits and miscellaneous organic matter that Wimsey had ferried in from the great outdoors. My apartment reeked of both hound stink and intestinal gas.

And Wimsey was the gift that kept on giving. For a week after his visit, whenever I took a shower the drain trap filled with hair. His.

But worst of all, although I had failed to make progress training Wimsey, I had the unsettling feeling that the reverse could not be said to be true.

CHAPTER 12--PRACTICE MAKES IMPERFECT

The next month flew by in a whirl of activity. Maria received the welcome news that the Westminster Kennel Club Dog Show was once again prepared to endure Wimsey in its midst and I, having managed to completely block out the debacle that was Thanksgiving, decided it would be a good idea to work with him on his show ring skills.

Of Wimsey's many deficiencies as a show dog, the one that seemed most amenable to remediation was his propensity to pace rather than to trot. And while Wimsey found this system of locomotion exceptionally agreeable-- probably because no one else did--using both legs on the same side of his body made him look less like a potential Best in Show and more like a canine creation of Dr. Frankenstein.

I did some research on the issue and several of the dog show books recommended the use of cavalettis, the low trotting poles used to train horses and agility dogs. That was helpful but as New York City is not overly supplied with equine supply stores, I had no idea where to get them. Fortunately, Beverly, the ASPCA's volunteer coordinator, knew how to construct them using 4-foot long PVC poles with 3-inch high pipe connectors at each end from Home Depot.

After a quick trip to the store and even quicker assembly I now had fifteen cavalettis. What I didn't have was a way to get them across the street to Riverside Park. They were both heavy and slippery so carrying them was out of the question. I finally had the brilliant idea of putting them in my metal shopping cart. They all fit but I soon discovered that pushing a clattering cart filled with nothing but tall plastic pipes caused people around me to give me the wide berth usually accorded to those of unsound mind.

Maria and Wimsey were already waiting for me and Wimsey found the cavalettis to be of immediate interest. He bayed at them joyously and endeavored to extract one with his mouth. As I began to lay out these new chew toys at the recommended intervals Wimsey followed the process with an intensity seldom in evidence during our training sessions. And so did everyone around us. Speculation as to their purpose ran the gamut from ballet exercises to astronomy experiments. Wimsey just wanted to know what I was doing with his new toys. He wasn't happy when he found out.

I took his leash and positioned him at the head of the row.

"Wimsey, trot!" I commanded and tugged at him. He looked at me like I was the kind of person who pushed around shopping carts filled with plastic poles. Then he dropped to the ground and the end of a pole disappeared into his mouth. I removed the pole and dangled a piece of turkey over the row. Wimsey lunged for it and purely by accident stepped over the first pole. I walked forward keeping the turkey just out of reach. He tip-toed down the row like he was a Tennessee walking horse. When he had high stepped over the last one I rewarded him with the turkey and lavished him with praise that was totally unwarranted.

It was a start. Not a good one, but a start.

Two hours flew by with the speed of five. I did succeed in getting him to move faster--probably only because he realized that the faster he moved the faster he got fed--but his efforts definitely weren't going to win him any style points. He trotted over the poles with his head at right angles to his body keeping the turkey in view lest it escape to a location other than his mouth. It wasn't a good look for the show ring and neither was the Symphony for Annoyed Hound with which he accompanied it.

"Other than the baying and his head pointing the wrong way he seems to be getting the hang of it," I told Maria. "Let's see if he'll trot without the cavalettis."

We moved away from them.

"Wimsey trot!" I said. I sprang forward. Wimsey also sprang forward. I looked down. He was pacing.

"I don't think he understands," Maria observed with classic understatement.

"He's not the only one," I replied.

But Wimsey's daily and sometimes nightly cavaletti practice (otherwise known as The Wimsey Cavaletti Show, a raucous musical comedy in far too many acts) spawned an idea that turned out to increase Wimsey's notoriety even further. Cavaletti practice was very popular in the neighborhood and was watched both by people in the park and by those in the apartments across the street. Wimsey and I were often stopped by audience members telling us how enjoyable it was so I decided that he should blog about it. The blog was called *Diary of a Manhattan Bloodhound,* and Wimsey soon branched out to include not only cavaletti practice but all the other ways in which he made Maria and I look foolish. He was never short of material.

The weekend before Westminster, Maria borrowed her friend Ray's car and we drove out to New Jersey so Diane and Wimsey's co-breeder, Lily, could inspect him.

"He's in great condition," Lily observed as she eyeballed him. He ought to be considering the state of Maria's hamstring and my shoulder. But it was good to know that we hadn't sacrificed our body parts in vain.

"Diane, take him," Lily said, "I want to see him move."

Diane took him. She gaited him back and forth. Lily's brow wrinkled.

"What's he doing with his feet?" she asked. "I can't tell whether he's trotting or pacing."

Neither could we.

Wimsey had invented a new gait. We called it The Trop.

Westminster was soon upon us and the only good thing about it was that Wimsey was benched in the main area with the other bloodhounds. If anything, he looked even worse than last year. He carried his tail at zero mast and it threatened to tuck at any moment. But outside of the ring, he once again behaved like he was competing for Mr. Congeniality. His appeal was further enhanced by the fact that he had fallen deeply in love with Bizzy, the lady hound in the crate next door, and spent much of his time crooning romantic ballads for her edification. And if last year's *Best in Show* moment was driven by Wimsey's media attention, this year's occurred because everyone, except those who knew anything about bloodhounds, assumed that Wimsey was this year's Breed winner. It was a mistake that did not sit especially well with the owners of the dog who had actually won Best of Breed. They alternated between looking daggers at us and glaring at the crowds who gathered in front of Wimsey's crate.

As Maria and I waited out the time to our release, we reviewed the situation. It was true that Wimsey hadn't paced or unleashed The Trop on the show world, but he hadn't looked much like Wimsey either. We were both mystified and frustrated.

"Maybe we should show him ourselves," I suggested.

It seemed like a good idea at the time. But then again, so did all my other ones.

CHAPTER 13--WHO'S HANDLING WHOM

Although neither Maria nor I knew anything about handling a dog in the show ring we did know that Wimsey was perhaps not the most promising of material with which to embark on a maiden show handling career. I had a lot of experience handling dogs for the ASPCA both on television and at charity events, but dog shows were something completely different so a trainer at the ASPCA suggested we take a private show handling class from an instructor she knew in Westchester.

Maria once again prevailed upon her friend Ray to lend us his car, and since Wimsey was convinced that his proper place was in the front seat, she also went out and bought him a car harness. This turned out to be a formidable looking contraption with a zip line that attached to each of the rear door hooks and a connector line that clipped onto a thick black leather harness that made Wimsey look more like he was about to join a motorcycle gang than go for a ride in a car. After following all the instructions assiduously and clipping Wimsey to the zip line exactly as they directed we took our places in the front seat. We had just begun to bicker about the best route to take when Wimsey, who never approved of any argument of which he was not the cause, decided to settle the matter by climbing into Maria's lap and sitting on the map.

"I think the harness has a design flaw," Maria observed. "But at least it will still stop him from going through the windshield." I couldn't really hear her because Wimsey had pressed his neck into her face so he could hang his head out the window.

When we arrived—having first convinced Wimsey that we weren't going anywhere unless he returned to the back seat—we were met by a kind but firm-looking woman. We introduced ourselves and she ushered us into a large training room. Then she gave Wimsey an indulgent pat on the head as he tried to nose wand her in an overly familiar manner and handed me a leather loop of unsurpassed flimsiness.

"The important thing," she informed me, "is to position the show lead high up on the neck, right behind the ears so you can maintain control." I slipped the lead over Wimsey's head. He shook. It disappeared into a piece of dewlap.

"Now, let me see you trot him once around the ring," she said with what I considered to be undue optimism. But pacing was the least of my problems. Wimsey suddenly realized that there now appeared to be few impediments to him doing anything he wanted to do so he gleefully galloped off to do them. I pulled him out from under a pile of agility equipment and choked up on the show lead so much that my hand was practically resting on his neck. Then I moved forward cautiously, hoping to get a sedate trot. I got a sedate pace. I handed the lead to Maria.

"Here, you try," I said. He took off with her around the ring. She handed me back the lead. She was panting.

Goldilocks had nothing on Wimsey—if we took off too slowly, he paced; if we took off too fast, he galloped. The only way to get him to trot was to hit a middle speed with a precision that made achieving it both improbable and impractical.

"I think you should practice taking off fast and let Wimsey gallop a few strides and then take back on him just enough to ratchet him down a notch to a trot," our instructor suggested.

It was a sensible plan, but Wimsey ate sensible plans for breakfast. If we took back on him too much, he paced; if we took back on him too little, the rodeo continued.

We moved on to stacking. I bent down and tried to move Wimsey's front leg. It wouldn't budge. He had shifted all his weight onto it. I reached for the other one. That one wouldn't move either. He had shifted his weight as soon as I touched it. The instructor looked down at me with pity.

"Not like that," she said, in a way that suggested I was a few neurons short of the usual complement. "You have to grab his leg above the elbow or else you won't be able to move it." I had already figured out the not moving part. I did as she instructed and I was thrilled to see that I could move Wimsey's legs. Unfortunately, Wimsey could also move Wimsey's legs. And he did. Right back to where they had originally been.

We moved on.

Next up was free stacking. After trotting down and back for the judge, a dog is supposed to stop in a perfect stack without any handler intervention. In Wimsey's case it just involved stopping.

"It will take practice," our instructor informed us over the sound of Wimsey baying at her for more of the $50 bag of bait she had in her hand.

After class, Maria turned to me.

"Well that went well," she said. "He's all yours in the ring."

The next week, rejecting the $50 bag of bait in favor of something Maria didn't have to work a second job to afford, I procured a large and revolting beef liver from

Fairway, our local and much hated grocery store. Maria baked and prepared it according to the recipe she found in one of our show books with the result that her apartment now reeked of both hound and liver. It was a tossup which of us had the worse assignment.

Armed with baked liver and a show lead we now began to conduct impromptu show dog practice sessions in Central Park. It soon became apparent that Wimsey considered his show lead to be an inconsequential piece of string around his neck and as soon as I slipped it on he believed himself to be at liberty to do whatever. The whatever mostly consisted of him taking off with me in pursuit of a squirrel or some other equally engaging social opportunity. It goes without saying that Wimsey's show dog practice was not popular with our fellow dog owners. Being galloped at by a dog of Wimsey's size trailing a human with no discernible means of stopping him other than yelling "He's friendly! He's friendly!" was understandably unnerving. Before every practice session Maria and I scanned the horizon anxiously like sailors on a galleon in pirate infested waters. There are few sounds are more terrifying than that of "squirrel!" or "dog!" when one is holding onto Wimsey with a show lead. Our only remedy was to throw ourselves on top of him and hope for the best.

But every rule has its exception and one day I actually wanted Wimsey to take off with me.

Wimsey had as usual been dragging me through Central Park for what was euphemistically known as his afternoon walk when we paused at the base of Cherry Hill. A man came running towards us.

"Miss! Miss!," he called out "can we use your dog?! We're shooting a commercial for Cynthia Rowley."

"What do you want him to do?" I asked cautiously. I still hadn't recovered from Wimsey's last attempt at modelling. The man explained that it was supposed to be a humorous ad that involved a model running and hiding behind large things—boulders, trees shrubs, etc., and given Wimsey's size, they thought it would be hilarious if she hid behind him as well.

"So really," the man continued "all he would have to do is walk across this field and let the model crouch down and creep beside him." On the surface, this did not appear to be beyond even Wimsey's limited skill set.

"OK," I said.

"Great! Can you take off his leash?"

"Not unless you want to film him in another state," I replied. "But his leash is twenty feet long, so I should be able to keep out of camera range."

I positioned Wimsey at one end of the field. The model was crouched behind a nearby rock ready to scamper and hide behind him.

"Action!" yelled the director. I started across the field.

"Cut!" yelled the director. I looked down. Wimsey was heeling.

"We need the dog to walk ahead of you," he called out.

That much was obvious but Wimsey stood next to me looking uncharacteristically casual. For once he seemed to have no pressing olfactory business that required his presence somewhere we weren't. I wrestled with him a bit hoping to rile him up.

"Let's go!" I loudly urged. Words that had never before passed my lips.

Wimsey walked next to me like he was epoxied to my left hip. Obviously since I wanted him to drag me across the field his best course of action was not to. After all, anything could be at the end of that field—a bathtub, the nail clippers, ear cleaning solution…. And compliance in one thing might lead to compliance in other, more horrifying things, like sit stays.

I conceded defeat and went over to apologize to the director and the crew. It was just then that Wimsey noticed that a crew member was holding his favorite brand of plastic water bottle. He bayed loudly at him. When I explained why he was baying the man kindly dumped out the water and gave Wimsey the bottle. Now in possession of his prize, Wimsey suddenly felt a compelling need to be elsewhere. He galloped across the field like he was being chased by a vet with a rectal thermometer.

"I hate you" I called after him.

But I doubt if he could hear me—he was twenty feet away.

CHAPTER 14--WIMSEY AT HIS TOILETTE

After managing to survive multiple park and cavaletti practice sessions, we were finally ready (ish) to take our show on the road. But where? Maria and I began to scour the dog show listings on infodog.com in search of a show in the Tri-state area that we could drive to easily--to the extent that anything involving either driving or Wimsey was easy. In spite of the fact that I studied the directions for pumping gas like a scholar with a Dead Sea Scroll, my abilities in this area were minimal and the driving experience was not enhanced by the fact that Wimsey had decided that he liked to supervise the activity with his front feet on the gear shift.

We chose a large outdoor show in Trenton, New Jersey and our next problem was how and where to get Wimsey groomed. In the interval since Westminster

Wimsey's regular groomer had exited the business (hopefully not because of Wimsey) and none of the other establishments in the neighborhood were capable of dealing with either an animal of his size or with one holding his strong views on the subject of blow dryers. The only solution seemed to be to bathe him ourselves, and since Wimsey was too large to fit into Maria's doll-sized bathroom, I unexpectedly found myself in the Wimsey dog grooming business.

In preparation for this new adventure I purchased a detachable spa showerhead, a large number of rubber mats for both the tub and the bathroom floor to prevent Wimsey from slipping and to prevent any bathwater tsunamis from flooding the floor below, five new bath towels (including an expensive, super-absorbent microfiber one), a pound of bribing turkey and a seventeen-inch bully stick to keep Wimsey occupied while he air dried in a location that was not my bed or my lap. I also bought a bottle of cachaça for cocktails. I had a feeling we were going to need them.

Wimsey charged into my apartment with an energy born of his high expectations for another highly successful visit. No doubt he had a list of new things he wanted to teach me to do for him. But this enthusiasm rapidly turned to suspicion as he watched Maria unpack not toys, bones and treats, but towels, Crown Royal Finishing Spray, a bottle of expensive, shih-tzu sized organic dog shampoo and a chamois cloth that a dog show book had assured us would make Wimsey's coat shine like a mirror ball. Wimsey took one look and decided he had urgent matters to attend to in my shoe closet.

Maria and I changed into t-shirts and shorts and after extracting Wimsey with a slip chain and a short leash, I made encouraging noises about all the fun to be had in the bathroom. He looked at me skeptically. He seemed to sense that whatever fate awaited him on the other side of the bathroom door was not one of which he was going to approve. On the other hand, there was the distinct smell of turkey that wafted from the bag I had left on the side of the tub. He caved and followed me into the bathroom.

I handed the bag to Maria.

"Feed it to him very slowly," I said once I had used it to lure him into the tub.

I picked up the spa showerhead and turned the spray to maximum. The water rolled off Wimsey's back like he was made of wax paper.

"He's not even wet. How is that possible?" Maria exclaimed.

I knew what she meant. Wimsey's fur got soaked in even the slightest of drizzles. While I contemplated the mysteries of a suddenly water-proof dog, Wimsey alternated between sucking down turkey like a participant in hot dog eating contest and making athletic attempts to exit the bathtub. I quickly dumped the bottle of shampoo on him and began to scrub. He seemed to be ignoring me but somehow every time I tried to lather up his hind legs or his underside he sat down so I couldn't. And while I battled Wimsey's recalcitrant hind end Maria was having an even worse time with the front one. Having become deeply dissatisfied with the slow pace of turkey feeding he tried to accelerate matters by alternately ramming her with his dripping snout and thwacking her with his dripping paws. And no sooner had I succeeded in working up the shampoo into its promised rich, creamy and organic lather than he wound up like a pitcher on the mound and it landed with a rich, creamy and organic splat all over us. Then taking advantage of Maria's temporary blindness he made a grab for the turkey.

When I was finally able to see again, I began scrubbing and rinsing with a vigor that caused large clumps of his fur to detach themselves and lodge in the drain trap. The water level slowly rose and as soon as it reached Wimsey's ankles he bolted for dry land like a character in the *Poseidon Adventure*. Maria threw herself on top of him while I dived for the drain to try to remove some of the rapidly accumulating thickets.

"I'm out of turkey," Maria informed me once the crisis had been averted.

"I told you to feed him slowly!"

She glared at me through a sticky mixture of soap, itchy hound hair and partially masticated turkey bits. I shut up. I rinsed quickly.

"Let's see if we can get him to shake," I suggested when he was finally suds free. We blocked Wimsey's exit, held towels in front of ourselves and waited expectantly. Lacking any soap to fling in our faces, he just stood there dripping water and looking at us blankly. I grabbed his facial wrinkles, Maria grabbed his body wrinkles and we began to wring him out like a baggy sweater. He thoroughly enjoyed this, feeling no doubt that it was a vast improvement over his near death from drowning.

"OK, Wimsey, shake," I said. But Wimsey did not shake. He was too busy trying to access the empty turkey bag to see if it had been replenished by the Turkey Fairy. I ruffled his hair against the grain. He looked like an annoyed woodpecker. A very wet one.

"He's not going to shake. Let's just let him out and dry him," Maria said. We stepped aside. Wimsey climbed out. Wimsey shook. Hair, drool and turkey bits went flying.

"He's such a jerk," I muttered as I wiped my face.

"I think he knows," Maria replied.

We each grabbed a large fluffy towel and went to work.

"Nothing's happening!" Maria exclaimed.

It was true. Wimsey's fur, so resistant to moisture only an hour earlier, now retained it with the avidity of a sponge. The new microfiber towel was reduced to a sodden mess on the floor. While we continued our futile attempts to dry him, Wimsey occupied himself in a round robin of trying to inhale the empty turkey bag, investigating the area under my sink and scratching at the closed door. And whenever he noticed that the towels were not in contact with his body, he shook. It was like being confined in a small space with a wet porcupine. One by one our pile of dry, fluffy towels joined their microfiber cousin on the floor.

"Let's let him out. Maybe he'll dry better in the air," I suggested. Sensing that freedom was imminent and out of patience with both the incessant toweling and disgraceful lack of snack possibilities, Wimsey threw himself at the closed door with the force of a small tank.

"OK, OK, I'll let you out," I said. I pulled on the door. Nothing happened. I twisted the doorknob in the opposite direction and yanked. Sill nothing. Maria tried. She pulled, twisted and kicked. Nothing.

Wimsey had locked us in the bathroom.

"What are we going to do!?" Maria cried, panic rising in her voice. As much as she loved her hound the prospect of being entombed with him in a bathroom lacked a certain charm. Wimsey, too, wondered what we were going to do. He had gotten bored with trying to lift the sink off its legs and had begun to scratch at the door in earnest.

I decided that both the problem and the solution lay in physics.

"Well, probably the heat has caused the door to expand which caused it to jam, so when it cools down it will contract and then it should open," I said.

Sometimes having a science education was not an advantage.

My explanation as to the cause of our predicament may well have been true but it was more likely due to the canine cannonball that had slammed into the door. And the solution, just like the cause, was literally staring me in the face. I looked at the door. Somehow I had never noticed that it had a long, oblong ventilation cutout at the bottom. I hooked my arm under it and yanked. The door flew open and Wimsey flew out. I turned to Maria who was now grinning.

"I never want to hear about this again," I said with a red face. And while I may never have heard about the incident again, everyone else did.

We celebrated our escape with caipirinhas and a meal of such lavishness that when it was finished Wimsey looked like a python that had swallowed a goat.

When he was finally mostly dry—I don't believe he was ever fully dry until the next morning—we doused him with Crown Royal and rubbed his coat with the chamois cloth until we could practically see our faces in it. Maria bent down and sniffed.

"You can't even smell his hound stink!" she exclaimed.

We both buried our faces deep in Wimsey's fur and snorted.

It was as exhilarating as cocaine and probably not much cheaper.

CHAPTER 15--SHOW DOG WIMSEY GOES TO TRENTON

I presented myself at Maria's apartment bright and early the next morning carrying my new show clothes, the centerpiece of which was a pair of hunter green trousers chosen more for their ability to flatter the color of Wimsey's coat than for the contours of my backside. But sacrifices had to be made (although never of course by Wimsey) and however delighted he was to see me he went berserk as soon as his motorcycle gang harness made its appearance.

"It's amazing isn't it," I observed to Maria, "that Wimsey can't seem to make the connection between trotting and turkey but seems to have no difficulty making the connection between that harness and a ride in the car."

"Well it's still better than him knowing that when I brush my teeth at night I'm going to bed so it's time for him to get up on it and make me wrestle him for it."

Once leashed and harnessed, Wimsey propelled himself into Ray's little SUV reeking of Crown Royal in which I could already detect the faint yet unmistakable odor of resurgent hound stink. So much effort for so little result. I just hoped that his performance in the show ring wouldn't be the same story. In any case, it was a beautiful day for a drive, which was a good thing considering how many times I managed to get us lost. And like so many other things, it was a circumstance appreciated by Wimsey but by no one else.

The show was being held at The Mercer County Fairgrounds, which turned out to be a large pastoral setting with wide open fields upon which a sizeable number of rings, tents, vendor booths and food stalls had been erected. Attendees, both human and canine, bustled about, the latter of whom were all walking politely on flimsy show leads. I sighed and decanted Wimsey into his Halti, a circumstance to which he objected vociferously. Prong collars are forbidden anywhere on the grounds of a dog show and although I wasn't sure about Haltis I was also sure that I didn't want to end up face down in the dirt. But my views on the matter cut little ice with Wimsey and he was busy trying to get the strap off his nose when I saw a small blonde woman approach.

"Hi I'm Chris," she said. "We're showing our bloodhound Brady today also." She stared at Wimsey who, having failed to liberate himself from the Halti, was now letting me and everyone else know what he thought about my choice of equipment.

"Wait a minute, isn't this the dog with the blog?" she asked. "He's so funny!" Those were not exactly the words I would have used to describe Wimsey at that moment. Having been unsuccessful in either ripping the Halti from his head or in getting me to remove it for him he was now throwing a tantrum on the ground.

"Thanks," I said. "It's nice to know someone finds him amusing." Obviously the reading of it was much funnier than the living of it.

"Here, hang onto him, "I said to Maria and handed her Wimsey's leash once Chris had trundled off to deal with Brady related matters. "I'm going to find the bathroom to change. I'll meet you at the ring" The bathroom turned out to be quite a hike but even at that distance and through the door of the stall I could still hear Wimsey. I changed quickly.

The ring area was packed and I had to plow my way through a mass of people and dogs to find the one that was ours. Then suddenly the crowds parted and Wimsey appeared. He was wearing his show lead and dragging Maria behind him like an inconvenient piece of baggage. He erupted to announce the news of his "find" as soon as he saw me. I had to shout my number to the ring steward multiple times and at escalating volumes.

"Here, help me get my number pinned on," I said to Maria, when I was at last able to make myself heard above Wimsey. "My hands are shaking."

"But you're always so calm," she said. "Even when you handle shelter dogs on TV."

"Yeah but none of them were Wimsey," I replied as he bayed and tried to exploit the deficiencies of his show lead by introducing himself to all the other dogs in the vicinity.

I listened anxiously for my number and as soon as it was called I moved forward. Wimsey immediately tried to perform an examination of a proctological nature on the dog just ahead of us. Its handler was not amused. I piloted Wimsey to our spot against the rail and took a deep breath. It was time to stack him. I reached over and tried to adjust his front left leg the way I had been taught. And I was still trying to adjust his front left leg the way I had been taught when the judge swept past us for her first look at the lineup. Everyone else's dog was stacked perfectly.

It was a large class and since we were stationed towards the back of it I decided to use the time until the judge's examination to practice stacking. I reached over and this time I was able to correctly place Wimsey's front left leg. But when I reached for the front right one the left one slid back to its original position. I thought maybe moving faster would help. It didn't. Around and around his four legs we went playing stacking Whack-a-Mole. Every time I stepped back to check my work, Wimsey's feet were in exactly the same position as when I started. The only upside of the game was that it gave him something to do other than trying to drag me someplace we weren't supposed to be or behaving like the show ring was a dog park. Even so, every time the line advanced so did Wimsey's nose and threatened to insert itself into his neighbor's rectal regions. And if I tried to stop him by grabbing onto a piece of dewlap (the string around his neck apparently being for decorative purposes only) we wrestled. My white blouse, so crisp when I entered the ring now looked like it belonged in a wet t-shirt contest.

I had been so busy managing Wimsey that I hadn't realized that we were next in line for the judge. As the graduate of exactly one show handling class, I wasn't even sure of when exactly I was supposed to move him up into position. I took a wild guess and the change of scenery so delighted Wimsey that when I tried to stack him he danced around like a young Hibernian on St. Patrick's Day. There were a large number of handlers and spectators and I could feel them all watching me. It was like being in a play where you didn't know the lines. Given the expression on her face, the judge thought so too. The spectacle of a damp and disheveled handler trying to stack a dog with a bad case of happy feet was apparently not a pleasing one to the judicial eye. She gave me a piercing look and bent over to examine Wimsey. Wimsey returned the favor. When she stood up she had a trail of slime on her skirt.

"Down and back," she commanded drily. It was here that I thought we could redeem ourselves. Stacking had clearly been an epic fail, but I hoped that all the cavaletti practice with which we had entertained the neighborhood would now pay off. I took out a piece of liver and held it in front of Wimsey's twitching nose.

"Wimsey, trot!," I trilled gaily, hoping that he wouldn't decide to trop or treat the crowd to one of his lumbering Frankendog imitations. He took off at a gallop. Then having successfully navigated his down and back at warp speed, he thought it would be fitting finale to playfully mow down the judge. I was able to stop him by the slimmest of margins. And hoping for another crack at her he had stopped, not in a free stack, but in the stalking pose he usually adopted when laboring under the delusion that the capture of a squirrel was imminent. It didn't look like anything I had seen in a show ring before and probably not anything the judge had seen either. She stared at Wimsey. Then she stared at me. Then she snorted and turned away to examine a dog that did not have me as a handler. I slunk back along to rail to rejoin the line. Wimsey trotted happily beside me.

We didn't win.

Wimsey, unperturbed by his defeat, towed me out of the ring while giving voice like a hound on the hunt. I tried not to make eye contact with anyone. Some people gave me pitying looks, some people smiled and one lady tried to be encouraging,

"He's a pretty dog," she offered.

"It's my first time in the show ring," I replied.

"Yes, I kind of figured that," she said.

Wimsey stampeded his way over to Maria, ignoring any bodies that happened to be inconveniently placed in his path and alternated between baying in her face and smearing it with liver-scented slobber.

"Well, at least he didn't tuck his tail," I shouted above the din. On further reflection, Wimsey standing quietly with his tail tucked no longer seemed like such a bad thing.

But if Wimsey wasn't flavor of the month (or the day, year or week) in the show ring, as usual, the reverse could not be more true outside of it. Once clear of the ring area his loud and lively manner attracted large crowds of admirers. One of them happened to be a reporter for *The Trenton Times* and the next day, a highly sanitized account of Wimsey's show exploits appeared in the paper.

Wimsey was now officially the world's most successful unsuccessful show dog in history.

CHAPTER 16--ADVENTURES IN VETERINARY MEDICINE

Over the next several weeks, I summoned the courage to enter the show ring with Wimsey on two more occasions. Both shows were smaller and the results were only marginally less gruesome than those at Trenton. Having said that, in Oyster Bay Wimsey did manage to introduce a new and interesting variation by gaiting while both baying and with his nose pressed to the ground to follow the scent of a lady hound who was just coming into heat.

Nevertheless, we remained undaunted and were determined to persevere when our busy schedule of planned shows hit an abrupt and very unexpected speed bump. A week before our next show, Maria was sitting on the Tribute Couch (so named because Wimsey expected to be either fed or scratched any time he ascended it, an unfortunate side effect of my couch training), when Wimsey detected a vacancy in a lap that needed filling and climbed into it. Suddenly they were both covered in blood. Maria said it looked like Freddy Krueger had been performing open heart surgery. Wimsey, who always had a strong aversion to blood, particularly when it was his own, flew off her lap and into a panic. After a prolonged and gory chase, Maria managed to corner him and discovered, much to her relief, that the blood emanated from a small spot just above his right elbow.

I met them at the vet's office.

If Wimsey was famous (or infamous) on the Upper West Side, he was even more so at Riverside Veterinary Hospital where he was a regular and wildly popular customer. Apart from his obvious charm, much of this popularity stemmed from the fact that he allowed the staff to practice their craft freely upon whatever bit of him required it. They told us that he was a relaxed and cooperative patient, which was an alternative version of Wimsey that I longed to meet.

Wimsey, for his part, loved the staff's attention and admiration, which was a good thing because each week he seemed able to conjure up some new ailment that just like him was messy, expensive and inconvenient. And although these ailments were almost always of a non-serious nature, we did have one scare when Wimsey had to be whisked off for an X-ray of a suspected abdominal mass. The mass turned out to be a mound of undigested kibble. It was hardly surprising that Wimsey's digestive system hadn't yet gotten around to it given how much food he seemed able to pack away. Any dog capable of consuming fourteen cups of kibble, a slice of pizza, a cup of yogurt, a bag of turkey, a plate of scrambled eggs and then still have room to twitch his nose expectantly at Maria's dinner could not be expected to have a digestive system even remotely capable of keeping up. And somehow he never gained an ounce.

Wimsey's vet, Dr. F., much like his staff, also looked forward to Wimsey's frequent visits, but whether this was due to Wimsey's obvious affection for him or to Wimsey's obvious effect on his bank balance was unknown. In any event, on this occasion, Dr. F. informed us that Wimsey's Freddie Krueger episode was due to a weak spot in the skin above his elbow and would require several weeks to heal. We hit the pause button on Wimsey's show career.

Then shortly after Wimsey's elbow healed he began to limp. This time the culprit turned out to be a small cut on one of his pads. Dr. F. handed us a bottle of Nolvasan solution and told us to soak Wimsey's foot for ten minutes a day. Since Wimsey did nothing for ten minutes a day, at least not voluntarily and which did not involve either his nose or his naps, how to achieve this was a bit of a head scratcher. When I tried to immerse his paw in various containers and plastic bags the only thing that got soaked in Nolvasan was my kitchen floor. In the end we threw him into a daily Nolvasan-laced bath and plied him with ten minutes worth of turkey.

"Well, look on the bright side," I said to Maria one day as Wimsey mistook one of her fingers for a slice of turkey, "at least we don't have to get a urine sample." Maria shuddered. The very thought of anything to do with the collecting Wimsey's urine had that effect on her. The first time we tried it, we thought it would be easy. Dr. F.

handed Maria a urine collection kit consisting of latex gloves, a plastic container and antiseptic wipes.

"Remember, it's important to use the wipes to clean his prepuce and then to get a good midstream catch,' he instructed.

Maria was already an expert at prepuce cleaning owing to a pimple Wimsey once had on his penis that required her to do it twice a day. It was the only thing he ever allowed her to do.

While I walked Wimsey over to a likely looking tree Maria crouched coiled and ready to spring forward with the cup at the appropriate juncture. Wimsey, who ordinarily was keen to dispense urine freely and without limit over anything that was vertical and much that was not, did not seem to care much for the tree. He also did not seem to care much for any of the fire hydrants, garbage bags, trash bins and lampposts that I presented for his use. I couldn't even interest him in a parked bicycle, a normally forbidden and therefore much sought after target. He might sniff at something in a promising manner but as soon as he saw Maria creeping up on him with the cup he moved on.

Occasionally, just to keep her on her toes, he would lift his leg, wait until she got into position and then lower it again.

But there are limits, even to a seemingly infinitely large bladder like Wimsey's. So when Nature at last decreed an end to his policy of conservation of bodily fluids, he would select a spot so inconvenient that it required the skills of a contortionist to get a cup under him. And if Maria somehow managed to do so, Wimsey would expertly direct the stream away from the cup. And when she moved the cup, Wimsey moved the stream. It was like some unsanitary carnival game, that only Wimsey enjoyed playing and whose prize was not something anyone wanted to win. It took hours to get a urine sample.

Although urine collection was probably the most difficult challenge of Wimsey's vet care, it was by no means the only one. Getting pills down him was no picnic either. Wimsey was a human-sized dog which meant that treating his various ailments required either the largest pill available or multiple pills or frequently both. Although we both developed a variety of strategies, Maria always began with the direct approach. She would place the pill down Wimsey's throat and then massage his neck to induce him to swallow. The downside was that although Wimsey enjoyed the neck massage, he had only to wait until Maria was out of sight to hawk it up again and deposit it somewhere where it was unlikely to be found. And no matter how deeply we buried pills in balls of peanut butter, cream cheese, yam, meatballs or in bowls of his favorite fresh cooked foods, Wimsey had a talent for either consuming the food but not the pills or for warehousing them in his flews for later disposal. Checking his flews didn't always work either since they were abundantly supplied with multiple unhelpful folds and wrinkles. Whenever Maria and I cleaned our apartments we would invariably discover a treasure trove of Wimsey's ancient pharmaceutical discards. It was a wonder he ever got cured of anything.

But nothing prepared us for Wimsey's extreme antipathy towards an antibiotic called Baytril. He reacted to it like Maria was Lucrezia Borgia and he some inconvenient Medici. When she put it down his throat it immediately came flying back in her face. She managed to get one pill down him by hiding it in a Hound McMuffin--a large ball of ham, cheese and scrambled eggs--but a second dose remained untouched. If she tried imbedding it in a bowl of his favorite imported English rice pudding, he wouldn't even go near the bowl. We took him back to Dr. F. who administered a bank busting injection of Baytril and handed us a prescription for human cipro, a close pharmacological relative.

I took the prescription to a local Rite Aid where I had recently seen an ad touting the store's eagerness to fulfill all of Fido's prescription needs. I went up to the counter and handed the clerk a Rite Aid discount generic drug card with my name on it and the prescription with Wimsey's. The prescription had Riverside Veterinary Hospital printed in large letters at the top and Dr. F.'s name had a DVM after it. And if you still failed to get the point, the patient was "Wimsey Szabo (Canine)."

The clerk looked at the prescription and the card.

"We can't fill this for you," she announced in an officious tone. "Wimsey Szabo needs to be here in person to fill out a patient form. Tell him to bring his social security number and insurance card." Leaving aside the fact that telling Wimsey to do anything had an asymptotically low probability of success, in this case it was likely to be particularly ineffective.

"He's a dog," I replied. "Last time I checked he didn't have a social security number or an insurance card (although this was not strictly speaking true, Wimsey had better insurance than either Maria or myself which was probably the only reason we were still solvent). Also, I don't think he can read or write" (this was probably true, although when it came to Wimsey you never really knew what he was capable of). She glared at me, unwilling to back down.

"Let me check," she snapped and huffed off to the back. When she returned she was clearly not happy.

"OK," she admitted grudgingly. "We can fill it, but we need his date of birth on this form. I wrote it in and gave it back to her. Then she took both the form and Wimsey's prescription and scribbled "DOG!" in large and emphatic letters all over them.

About ten minutes later a lady in a white coat called Wimsey's name.

"Wait here," the lady said. "The pharmacist wants to speak to you about the need to avoid dairy products when you take this medication." Even apart from the clerk's dramatic notations, no one apparently seemed to find anything odd about the fact that my name was Wimsey Szabo (Canine). Perhaps they thought Canine was my maiden name.

"Wimsey Szabo is a dog and I promise not to feed him any yogurt, ice cream or gelato while he is on the medication," I replied. Wimsey was going to hate these dietary restrictions almost as much as he hated the Baytril.

"It's for a dog!" the woman yelled to the pharmacist. Lack of attention to detail is probably not an asset in a pharmacist. I made a mental note not to fill any of my own prescriptions here.

But this was not our first run-in with drugstore clerks--one refused to sell us the codeine pills Dr. F. prescribed for Wimsey's wrenched back because she told us that Wimsey could pulverize them and shoot up. But my favorite drugstore encounter was the one Maria had at Duane Reade.

It all started when we brought Wimsey to Dr. F. because we suspected that he was in the throes of yet another of his many anal gland infections. Wimsey was not known as "The Dog With the Golden Tush" for nothing and if his other veterinary visits paid for the vet's mortgage, his anus paid for a pool. Wimsey's tush was probably the most valuable thing either Maria or I owned. On this occasion, after getting the results of Wimsey's anal culture, Dr. F. had some bad news.

"Wimsey's culture shows the presence of antibiotic resistant bacteria," he informed us. "But I did some research and there seems to be one antibiotic that it's sensitive to. Unfortunately, it's only used in a type of non-veterinary eye wash."

He handed Maria a prescription.

"If you can find it, I'll use it to flush out Wimsey's anal glands and hope it does the trick."

Maria hurried off to Duane Reade and handed in the prescription. The pharmacy clerk handed her back a form asking for the patient's name, address, date of birth and telephone number. Maria filled it in, returned it and had a seat. A few minutes later, a different clerk called Maria's name.

"How old is your son," she asked.

"He's not my son, he's my dog," she replied, "and he's three."

"Well the medication is not approved for patients under five," the clerk explained, "and according to the form, he's under five."

"But he's a dog!" Maria exclaimed.

"How old did you say he was?" the clerk responded.

"He's three, but he's a dog. I don't think the age limit counts for dogs," Maria insisted.

The clerk disappeared. She returned with the pharmacist.

"The medication on the prescription is not approved for patients under five," he announced.

"But the patient is a dog" Maria countered.

"A dog?" he asked

"Yes, it's for a dog!' Maria affirmed.

"You're sure?" he asked. "A dog?"

Maria now became nervous that his next question was going to be about what the medication was going to be used for and that when he found out that it was going to be shot up Wimsey's rectum, he'd refuse to sell it to her.

"Really," she emphasized, "he's a dog. Wimsey Szabo is a dog!"

The pharmacist looked at her suspiciously, like maybe she intended to peddle ophthalmic solution to underage children on the street. He reluctantly returned to the realm of pills and potions and after a disquieting interval Maria heard Wimsey's name called again. But this time, much to her relief, the pharmacy clerk handed her a bag. She went to pay and while she was looking for her credit card, the cashier looked down at the bag.

"How old is your son," she asked with a concerned air.

"He's not my son, he's my dog," Maria answered once again nervous.

"A dog?" the clerk responded.

"Yes, A DOG!!!" she replied emphatically and then pulled out a wad of cash and hightailed it out of there before anyone else could tell her the medication wasn't for dogs under five. I crossed that pharmacy off my list too.

But Wimsey didn't earn his "Golden Tush" sobriquet solely on the basis of his anal glands. One day, Dr. F. delivered some additional bad news regarding Wimsey's expensive backside.

"Wimsey has a small anal fistula," he told us. "They don't usually heal on their own but before we consider surgery, I'd like to try cyclosporine ointment. It's a long shot, but we have nothing to lose." He failed to mention that what we had to lose was the $200 each small tube cost.

But even more shocking than the price was Wimsey's reaction to his new therapeutic regimen. It called for me to apply a warm, medicated compress to his anal region and then to carefully anoint it with the precious ointment several times a day. As soon as he spotted the bowl with the warm water, rather than attempting to insert himself into a shoe closet or to lift the bed off its legs in an attempt to make himself invisible under it, he lay down, rolled over and exposed the area to its fullest extent. While I compressed and anointed he snored blissfully.

"I swear he knows how much it costs," I complained to Maria.

Amazingly, after a king's ransom in ointment and against all the odds, the fistula healed. Although we knew that Wimsey could always be counted on to do the unexpected this was the first time it was actually something we liked.

But being subjected to a constant bombardment of Wimsey's eccentric ailments came at a cost that wasn't only monetary. Maria and I developed a paranoid tendency to see potential threats to Wimsey's health in some very unlikely places. One afternoon, Wimsey was taking a restorative break from trying to annihilate the squirrel population of Central Park and rolled over so we could rub his belly. Maria was about to oblige when she pointed and exclaimed with alarm,

"Look at Wimsey's testicles! There's something wrong with them—they're pointy."

I took a look. She was right. They were pointy. I was perplexed. Nothing in my stock of medical or veterinary knowledge covered any condition in which pointy testicles was a salient feature. I began to run through the possibilities—could there be abnormal growths that were causing the distortion to their shape?

"Why don't you palpate them and see if you can feel anything unusual," I suggested.

"I am not palpating Wimsey's testicles. And certainly not in public," she replied. "You do it."

"Uh, maybe later," I muttered.

"Well, one of us should palpate Wimsey's testicles. What happens if it's serious?"

She had a point. My concern for Wimsey's well-being overcame my squeamishness and I reached over and gently palpated Wimsey's gonads.

"They feel normal," I said. Although to be fair, I was not all that sure what Wimsey's testicles usually felt like.

I was just pondering this question when Wimsey decided that he was ready to resume his assault on the wildlife of Central Park. He rose and shook to rid himself of the dirt, grass and drool he had accumulated during his break. The shaking also caused all his folds and wrinkles to return to their proper places. As he dragged us forward we had a fine view of the area so recently under discussion. And there they were in all their ovoid, non-pointy glory—

the same magnificent orbs that were, if the many comments we received on the subject were anything to go by, the envy of much of New York City's male population.

Who knew that bloodhounds were baggy everywhere.

CHAPTER 17--A WALK IN THE PARK WITH WIMSEY IS NO WALK IN THE PARK

The upside of the veterinary-induced hiatus in Wimsey's show career was (at least from Wimsey's point of view) that he got to spend even more time in Central Park annoying its flora and fauna. He spent so much time there that tour guides on buses, pedicabs and foot began to point him out along with the Park's other major monuments. One of them even used to deliver a lecture on bloodhounds. I might as well have brought a mattress.

But spending so much time in Central Park did give me an entirely new appreciation for Wimsey's intellectual capabilities. Central Park has 843 acres and is crisscrossed by a complex web of paths and walkways, all of which Wimsey seemed to have no difficulty keeping in his head. Not only that, but like some chess grandmaster he used this knowledge to compute all possible combinations and permutations of paths that might eventually lead to the exits closest to home. It was an ability he used to devise elaborate countermeasures well in advance of any such outcome. He might, for instance, suddenly discover a scent so intriguing that he needed to follow its trail at the pace of an inchworm, one meticulous millimeter at a time. Or he might stop entirely to investigate a single blade of grass whose olfactory mysteries were such that they required an indefinite stay to unravel.

Wimsey's strategies didn't only depend on his nose, however. They very often involved people. Pretty much anyone doing anything would do. He once stood for twenty minutes fascinated by workmen repairing a walkway. A park employee raking leaves was like a sporting event gone into overtime. And if I failed to supervise him closely enough he would try to send it into double overtime by unraking the leaves as soon as the guy's back was turned.

But Wimsey wasn't always the spectator. Sometimes he was the one with the audience. If he didn't like the way the paths were heading, he had only to grab a stick and lay down to chew it and a crowd assembled like he had opened a show on Broadway. And any attempt on my part to bring down the curtain was poorly received by both Wimsey and his fans. Then when he had exhausted the entertainment possibilities of the stick, he would plunge into the crowd and greet its members one by one, which coincidentally had the effect of embroiling me in lengthy and delaying discussions that were all about him. And if no a prop like a stick or a water bottle was handy he would simply lay down in the grass and pose like a Sphinx. If I tugged on his leash he would roll over and wave his legs 180 degrees in the wrong direction which was even more popular than his stick chewing.

But tugging on Wimsey's leash, regardless of which way his feet were pointing, was something I did at my peril. It made people furious.

"Stop pulling on him! Lure him with a treat!" people would yell angrily at me.

The use of positive reinforcement is almost always a good idea but as I was learning, Wimsey had a singular talent for turning good ideas into bad ones. Assuming I presented him with a treat he was in the mood to eat at that moment he would follow it for all of twenty feet. Then he would grind to a halt until I gave it to him. I would produce another treat. Was it the right treat? Who knows. Wimsey changed his snack preferences faster than a chameleon changed colors. I had to try a selection from the assortment I always carried in my pouch until I found the magic one that he considered worth the effort of walking another twenty feet for. It was not lost on either of us that walking home twenty feet at a time offered little improvement over just staying in the park until he was ready to leave to commune with his food bowl. Or my bed. Or he wanted a cupcake from the bakery on Broadway. Or he wanted a cup of gelato. Or his nose detected the wafting scent of Jewelry Lady, the woman with the jewelry table on Broadway who fed him the brand of snacks that he would never accept from me.

Wimsey could give lessons in extortion to a Mafia don.

But sometimes the problem wasn't getting Wimsey to move but getting him to stop. Maria and I discovered this one steaming summer Sunday in Central Park when Wimsey decided he was hot and lay down under a leafy tree. Maria and I joined him. Wimsey abruptly changed his mind and rose to resume his walk. About five minutes later, he found another leafy tree and lay down. We again joined him. But again, as soon as our bottoms hit the ground, Wimsey's rose. The walk continued. Then Wimsey sat down. Then we sat down. Then Wimsey got up.

"He's doing it on purpose!" I exclaimed.

Sure enough, as long as we stood in the sun while he lounged in the shade, he was happy to stay put. He finally took all risk out of the equation and found a spot where there was no place for us to sit at all. We stood there under the broiling sun, the sweat running down our faces and watched Wimsey settle himself comfortably in his sylvan bower. Just then a woman approached us.

"What a beautiful dog!" she gushed. "And so well behaved."

Wimsey glanced up at us and thumped his tail. He looked like a Klingon. A very smug and triumphant one.

Wimsey's preferred method to beat the heat, however, wasn't under Central Park's trees but in its water. The Central Park Lake was his favorite spot for this probably because the fine for doing so was $200 (which he always endeavored to make four hundred by having me join him). But if Wimsey's lakeside ablutions were not popular with the Parks Department, they were enormously so with everyone else. Particularly people in rowboats. He liked to wade out to them to say hello. And when he returned to dry land those who had been watching onshore made generous contributions from their picnic baskets and lunch bags, undeterred by the fact that his dips frequently made him smell like a swamp and glow like an alien in a B movie from the algae that clung to his legs. And on very hot days there was even a conveniently placed dirt pile in which he could roll and insulate himself with a repulsive crust much of which eventually ended up in my face or on my couch.

Wimsey liked going to the lake.

But in addition to his career as a swim up bloodhound and impromptu picnic guest, Wimsey's park activities also included being a wedding crasher. He took an exceptionally strong interest in the many weddings that were held in Central Park and seemed to feel that his presence was essential to their success. Much to our surprise, the happy couple often agreed. And in spite of our terror at anything involving the color white, Wimsey made successful cameo appearances in a number of wedding photographs. And he made cameo appearances in another way as well.

The Ladies Pavilion is a scenic open-air structure that abuts the lake and is a popular spot for weddings. Wimsey made it a point to look in there on a regular basis.

Picture the scene:

Before us stands a lovely bride decked out in white nuptial splendor. Next to her, stands a striking groom attired in an elegant morning coat. Friends and family are arrayed at their sides, drinking in the delicate tracery of the Victorian pavilion juxtaposed with the modern majesty of the New York skyline rising in the distance. In the foreground, we see the officiant, incanting the solemn words of the wedding service as the couple prepare to take the vows that will cement their love and join them together for an eternity.

And then suddenly, we hear… the sound of ….BAYING!!! Resounding, raucous, reverberating and joyous BAYING!

Wimsey never understood why I dragged him away. It probably made him bay even louder.

I always hoped that the bride and groom had a good sense of humor. And their videographer a good sound editor.

CHAPTER 18--NEW YORK AND WIMSEY'S FINEST

Wimsey was a dog with a large number of idiosyncratic obsessions. In addition to weddings and rowboats he was also obsessed with things such as plastic water bottles, tourists, The American Museum of Natural History, the Apple Store, construction sites, automobiles, The Boat Basin Café, the Time Warner Center, the tuna sandwiches at the Boathouse, something we called Endless North (his determination to go indefinitely north on Columbus Avenue) and pedicabs and their drivers. The pedicab one was at least useful since his baying attracted paying customers instead of horrified stares.

But no obsession was stronger than Wimsey's passion for police officers. It was a love that began almost immediately upon his arrival in New York as a young puppy. One night after work Maria decided to try to teach

Baby Wimsey to sit and stay using a method she had read about in a training book. The idea was to put the puppy into a sit and then walk around it in circles while encouraging it to remain seated. Maria took Wimsey to Riverside Park, found a suitable area in a small concrete plaza and began the exercise. She circled Wimsey with all her attention entirely focused on making sure that he stayed put. Suddenly she heard a voice.

"Miss, can we help you get home?"

The voice belonged to police officer. He exited his vehicle and approached her cautiously. It was dark. Wimsey was small. He was mostly black. The officers didn't see a woman training a dog. They saw a woman walking erratically in circles. Was she drunk? High? Mentally unbalanced? Or the owner of a bloodhound puppy with an infinitesimally short attention span. The officer may have been mistaken in what he saw but Wimsey certainly wasn't. He emitted a yip of delight and launched his wiggling body at the officer's legs.

It was the beginning of a beautiful, if spectacularly inconvenient, friendship.

The 20th Precinct was located directly on Wimsey's route to and from Central Park and while this made for a safe neighborhood it did not make for a peaceful walk. Wimsey laid loud siege to it at every opportunity. His usual method was pretty straightforward—he just lunged for the door baying furiously. But then every so often he would put his nose to the ground and approach the building as if he were so in engrossed in the scent he was following that he failed to notice its proximity. "Aha," I would think to myself, "he's finally outgrowing his obsession with it." And just like Charlie Brown and the football, as soon as I lengthened his leash and relaxed my grip-- bam! I would go flying painfully towards the entrance. He got me every time.

But it wasn't just the police in the precinct that drew Wimsey's interest. He tracked police officers all over the city with a tenacity that exceeded even that with which he tracked people eating pizza or crews shooting movies. And when he found them he would bay, throw himself against their legs and do unsanitary things to their uniforms until they petted him. He sometimes even stood on his head, a maneuver that involved putting his head on the ground, his rump in the air and spinning. It was his highest accolade.

And if the officers happened to be in a patrol car, he believed it was possible for him to fit through its window and would shove whatever bit of himself he could through even the smallest of openings. He may not have been able to get into the car but his efforts to do so did entertain its occupants. They showed their appreciation with their breakfasts, lunches, dinners and snacks.

And then one day Wimsey hit the jackpot. He was carrying on as usual in front of the Precinct when a distinguished, white-haired gentleman emerged. It was the Precinct Commander.

"Is this the dog my officers are always talking about?" he asked.

"Unfortunately yes," Maria replied.

"Well then, he had better come in." The gallant gentleman opened the door and personally escorted us into the squad room. It was perhaps the happiest day of Wimsey's life, possibly even eclipsing the day he dragged me face first into a snowbank. Wimsey wiggled parts of himself that I hadn't known could be wiggled.

Word about Wimsey's visit spread and it increased his stature and notoriety amongst the constabulary even further. Officers started rolling up behind us and blaring "Hello Wimsey!" through their bullhorns. I jumped. Wimsey wagged. He liked hearing his name amplified. But he especially liked it when the officers used their bullhorns to bay at him. He happily joined them in a deafening duet that was probably appreciated more by the participants than by the neighborhood.

But bullhorns could also come in extremely handy. One day Wimsey and I were crossing the treacherous intersection of Riverside Drive and the West Side Highway. We were in the middle of the street when I saw with a rush of adrenalin that a car had run the red light and was heading straight for us. Suddenly a bullhorn from a nearby patrol car sprang to life.

"HEY BLUE CAR!" it blared. "DON'T RUN OVER MY FRIEND!" The officer wasn't talking about me. But the car stopped.

And just like any New York celebrity, Wimsey's fame earned him special privileges. The entrance to Central

Park was all too often blocked by police barricades because of parades or other special events on Central Park West. These restrictions, however, seldom applied to Wimsey. As soon as the officers heard the sound of his voice there were shouts of "It's Wimsey, let him through." The barriers would fall and a phalanx of officers would step forward to provide him with an honor guard across the street. Other celebrities stopped traffic; Wimsey stopped parades.

Maria and I often debated the question of how, in a sea of scent like New York, Wimsey managed to identify those belonging exclusively to police officers. Our working theory was that their uniforms must have a distinctive odor that Wimsey found insanely noseworthy.

Like so many of our other theories concerning Wimsey, this one, too, turned out to be wrong.

One Sunday the three of us were headed south after a lengthy excursion to the quieter, northern reaches of Central Park. Suddenly Wimsey spun around and stared fixedly at a hill behind us. He began to bay.

"What's he baying at?" I asked Maria, as Wimsey towed me across the street in the direction of the hill.

"I don't know," she replied. "Maybe it's that car up there. Do we know the guy standing next to it?" I squinted at the figure in the distance.

"I don't think so, but maybe Wimsey does."

This was not an uncommon occurrence given how many people we met and that Wimsey was much better at remembering scent than we were at remembering faces. Meanwhile Wimsey plowed ahead, aiming, just as Maria had predicted, straight for the car and the large man standing next to it. I looked around. We were in a very quiet and rather deserted section of the park and it crossed my mind that this was not perhaps the smartest thing to be doing. On the other hand, there were three of us and one of them was a behemoth of a dog. The fact that Wimsey's idea of protection was to barricade himself behind our legs was generally overshadowed by the intimidation factor inherent in an animal of his size. I hoped this would be the case today.

As we got closer, I saw that there were two other men in the car. "Not good," I thought. I was just speculating as to what unsavory business they might be up to and whether we should turn around when Wimsey bayed and launched himself ecstatically against the big man's legs.

"I'm sorry," I said, eyeing the guy, "he just wants to say hello. Have you met him before?"

"No, but what a great looking dog," he enthused as he massaged a section of dewlap with a vigor that its recipient clearly found immensely pleasing. It was when the man reached over to find a more advantageous spot that I saw it. He had a gun. For a second my heart stopped. Maria also saw it, but she came to a much different conclusion.

"Excuse me," she said, "but can I ask, are you a police officer?"

"Yeah," he answered. "We're working undercover. There's been some drug activity up here. How'd you know?"

"I didn't. He did," she replied pointing to Wimsey who was now a leaning, drooling and grunting bundle of wrinkled ecstasy. "He adores police officers."

At this point, Wimsey, suddenly became aware that he was two officers short of a petting quorum and began to stare at the car. He bayed some encouragement at it. One of the men got out and did his duty but the other remained firmly rooted to his seat. Wimsey, clearly disturbed by such a blatant dereliction, dragged me over to the car and increased the volume of his summons. Perhaps he thought the guy hadn't heard him.

"C'mon," Wimsey's second victim called to the man in the car, "he just wants you to pet him." Then he turned to me. "He's afraid of dogs," he explained.

"We understand," I replied, and hauled an extremely annoyed Wimsey out of terror range and down the hill.

"I guess Ray was right," Maria observed as we continued our walk. Ray was a former police officer and his hypothesis was that it was the scent of gun oil that

Wimsey found so intoxicating and which enabled him to track and identify police officers. Even when they were undercover.

About ten minutes later, we saw the car containing Wimsey's new friends stopped at a red light. Wimsey bayed boisterously and dragged me over, eager to take up where he had left off. The guy who was afraid of dogs was driving, a circumstance that only seemed to fuel Wimsey's zeal. He stood up on his hind legs, thrust his mammoth head through the window and swished his tail violently back and forth. Much to our surprise Wimsey's reluctant quarry reached out and began to pet him.

I turned to Maria. "Just like the Mounties, Wimsey always gets his man."

CHAPTER 19--THE LOUD APPRENTICE

The phone rang with a call I never expected to get.

"Hello, Elizabeth. This is the _____ Agency--- you remember, from the J. Crew shoot."

How could I forget? I still had nightmares about it.

"Uh, yes," I replied, wondering if they were going to sue us.

"Would Wimsey be available next week to try out for *The Celebrity Apprentice*?"

My initial reaction was, "Wow, Wimsey on national TV!" quickly followed by, "Oh no, Wimsey on national TV!" I can only imagine how desperate for a bloodhound they must have been.

"What exactly would he have to do?" I asked slowly.

"We don't exactly know," she replied. "The contestants want a selection of dogs to choose from and we will be bringing other dogs to the audition but the task will involve only one dog." She emphasized the "one."

"OK," I replied. "Then we're available."

I immediately called Maria. She picked up the phone with "What's Wimsey done now?" When I broke the news to her, she was as astonished as I was.

"Don't they remember the last time?" was her first reaction followed by "Oh my God, what happens if they pick him! Can you imagine?"

Unfortunately, I could.

The following Saturday when Pet Chauffeur picked us up Wimsey was revved up and ready for action and I was revved up and regretting my decision. Nevertheless, I was not unprepared. I had rawhide bones, real bones, crunchy snacks, soft snacks, chewy snacks, a plethora of stuffed toys (although not Squeaky Teddy) and a pound of low salt turkey. I had no idea what Wimsey would try to do, but whatever it was I just hoped that at least one of these things would stop him from doing it.

The studio was located downtown on Union Square but I asked the driver to deposit us a few blocks away so Wimsey could stretch his legs. This mostly consisted of him stretching the rear ones upwards to announce himself to the neighborhood. Our progress was slow. When we were finally most of the way up 6th Avenue Wimsey stopped to sling some slingers that he felt needed to be slung. Absent a convenient couch he wound up to shake. Usually this was my cue to hurl myself on top of him to protect the innocent but since the current fling zone appeared to be devoid of any potential victims I merely stepped back and crossed my arms in front of my face. Wimsey shook. Suddenly there was a shout. I looked around to see where it had come from, but the street was empty. The only person visible was a man standing more than halfway back down the block and in a recessed doorway. He was wiping his face.

How Wimsey had managed to accomplish this feat I had no idea but I didn't intend to find out. While we didn't exactly run it was safe to say that there was a noticeable uptick in our progress. In spite of this, owing to Wimsey's many urinary calling cards, we were still the last to arrive and as we rounded the corner I saw a group of dogs and handlers already assembled in front of the building. Wimsey plunged in happily and was immediately captivated by a little bulldog puppy. He began to sniff it and prod it repeatedly with his snout. I looked up at its handler. He was scowling. It was the animal agent.

I pulled Wimsey off his pudgy little friend and exchanged his prong collar for what I hoped was a friendlier looking slip chain. It disappeared into his dewlap almost as fast as his nose disappeared back into the bulldog. There was large blob of drool on its head. I could feel the agent glaring at me as I wiped it off.

The baying began almost immediately thereafter. Its initial cause was that our entry into the building meant that I had to part Wimsey's nose from his puppy to which he appeared to have serious objections. But the baying continued in the elevator when Wimsey found his access to his other acquaintances blocked by my body. We lurched slowly and loudly upwards. When the door opened I unpinned Wimsey from the side of the elevator and he joined the rest of the pack surging down a long hallway. At the end of it was a large room that was littered with chairs, tables and assorted pieces of equipment and lounging members of the crew. Wimsey was understandably eager to poke his long nose everywhere it didn't belong and began to protest fiercely when I dragged him over to the row of chairs that had been set up for us along the back wall. All the other handlers sat as far away from us as possible.

When everyone was settled (except for Wimsey who had already climbed up on the chairs and was trying to walk along them to get to the other dogs), the animal agent disappeared. A few minutes later he returned with some very unwelcome news.

"They're not ready for us yet," he announced, "but the task is to film a commercial for Pedigree dog food. They haven't decided yet what the dog that's chosen will have to do," he said, eyeing Wimsey warily.

I suppose there could have been worse products that Wimsey might have been asked to endorse, but I had no idea what they could be. Even with food that was actually food Wimsey was notoriously finicky. He was like the Gordon Ramsey of the canine world and his culinary standards were just as strict: he would reject tuna fish in which there was either too much or too little mayonnaise; he would refuse to eat any of Maria's home-baked cinnamon rolls unless they had cream cheese frosting; pizza with insufficient cheese was anathema; and I once tried to feed him a piece of funnel cake from a food stall at a dog show that came flying out of his mouth at supersonic speed. Even his toothpaste had to be the one flavored like peanut butter and not poultry.

Wimsey's criteria with respect to the dimensions of his food were equally stringent. If I failed to cut his meat or his hard-boiled eggs into carefully calibrated bite-sized pieces he would deposit them by the side of his bowl with an accusatory glance. And although Wimsey was willing to eat most foods from a bowl, there were others, such as ice cream, gelato or yogurt that he wouldn't touch unless they were presented to him at the end of a spoon. And anything labelled "your dog will love it" (like the banana flavored anti-flatulence cream that made him flatulent) virtually guaranteed that Wimsey will hate it. Wimsey's demanding palate also made for some awkward social situations, as when some kind and generous soul on the street offered him a substandard snack and he spat it back at them. The exception being if I told them he wouldn't eat it he would consume it with relish.

And then there was the Infamous Marrow Bone Incident.

It all started when Beverly from the ASPCA gave me a bag containing a large, succulent frozen marrow bone for Wimsey. I knew from previous experience that if marrow bones were not actually the highest value treat you could possibly offer a dog, then they were pretty close. Wimsey had never had one and since bloodhounds can sometimes be a guardy breed I decided to take precautions in case he decided to do so.

I clipped a can of Spray Shield citronella spray to my belt in case Wimsey charged me; I placed a bag of turkey in my fanny pack to distract him in case he tried to bite me; I reviewed the procedure for how to quickly fashion a muzzle from a leash; and finally, I positioned a metal tray nearby in case I needed a physical shield.

When everything was ready, I brought Wimsey over to my apartment, suddenly aware of just how large and powerful a dog he was, especially in so small a space. I decided to take one more precaution and slipped his chain collar and short leash over his head to give myself more control in an emergency. Wimsey found this development to be of a highly suspicious nature and immediately took himself off to the shoe closet lest another encounter with his old nemesis, the bathtub, be in the offing. But when he saw me spread newspapers on the rug, his suspicion turned to excitement. And when I went to the refrigerator he began to dance, prance and squeak at me wildly.

I removed the marrow bone from the freezer and my fears seemed justified when he jumped and tried to snatch it from me. I body blocked him and placed the bone carefully in the middle of the newspapers. Then I backed away quickly. Wimsey approached the marrow bone. He sniffed it. He poked it. He gave it a lick. Then he turned on his heels and climbed up on the futon and went to sleep. And there I stood with my citronella spray, my turkey, my muzzle and my shield. I didn't know whether I was more embarrassed or more stunned.

The marrow bone remained there all afternoon like the cheese in the Farmer in the Dell.

When Maria arrived after work to pick Wimsey up, I told her what had happened (omitting the part about my precautions). She went over to take a look at the bone, which was now sitting in a sea of shredded newspapers. At least Wimsey had liked something.

"It's round," she said matter of factly.

"So?"

"He doesn't like bones that aren't bone-shaped."

Pedigree dog food wouldn't stand a chance. And neither would I.

Meanwhile the uneventful minutes of waiting ticked by with excruciating slowness until they became hours. The other dogs passed the time napping. Wimsey passed the time baying. It was a wonder any of them could sleep. He was bored. My bag of tricks failed to amuse him for long and soon a barnyard full of sacrificial stuffies and untouched rawhides (all bone-shaped) and cow bones (the only animal he would chew bones of), littered the floor around us. The only thing that seemed to interest him were the fuzzy microphone booms which he stared at, bayed at and lunged at. Whether he wanted to kill them or play with them remained a mystery, but what was not a mystery was that nothing I could do would induce him to shut up. When he was not baying at the booms, he was baying at the other dogs, or baying to explore the rest of the room, or just simply baying because he felt like baying. I offered him snacks, I offered him turkey, I scratched, pleaded and cajoled. Wimsey bayed on.

Periodically the animal agent shot me a dirty look. I noticed that he seemed curiously disinclined to try his hand at another intervention. But I'm sure that his already sour mood was not helped by being forced to listen to hours of Wimsey's Greatest Hits. No one's was, except for the crew's.

The crew, who like us, were also in waiting mode, seemed to find Wimsey an entertaining and welcome distraction. Wimsey generally had that effect on bored film and TV crews, so much so that he hunted them down on the streets of New York with an enthusiasm that other hounds reserved for small, juicy animals. The rewards of his unconventional hunt, however, were invariably rich and poured forth in attention, admiration and lavish tributes from the craft services catering truck. Absent a catering truck, today's crew supplied Wimsey with a steady stream of crunchy plastic water bottles that they never seemed to tire of watching him dismember. Or maybe it was the fact that he stopped baying while he did it.

In any case, it wasn't until I had been imprisoned with Wimsey for over six hours that the animal agent received word that they were finally ready for us. He herded us back down the hallway to a closed door at the other end of it where they were shooting. As we waited, the door opened and a guy poked his head out.

"Can you get him to stop making that noise," he said looking at me. "We can hear him inside."

The fact that they hadn't heard him before this was a testament to the sturdy construction of pre-war industrial buildings. I picked up the pace of the turkey feeding. It wasn't the case that Wimsey couldn't bay while eating—he could bay while doing most things—it was just that he chose not to. As long as I fed him fast enough. Even the smallest diminution in speed triggered the warning mini-bays which presaged the real thing.

Luckily for both me and the sound guy, Wimsey had not yet demolished all my turkey when the door opened and we were ushered in to meet the Men's Team. The room was large and alive with men milling around engaged in heated conversations all of which were being recorded by guys toting cameras and sound equipment. I angled Wimsey discretely away from the sound booms. None of the celebrity men were familiar to me but that wasn't really surprising. For one thing I was paying little attention to anything other than monitoring Wimsey for any resumption of the baying and for another, pop culture, like training Wimsey, was an area outside of my expertise. Nevertheless, I was happy that Wimsey didn't seem to consider that he needed to add a soundtrack to the proceedings.

At some point a tall gentleman with a cowboy hat and a southern drawl approached us and began to admire Wimsey. Whoever he was, he either thought a lot of Wimsey or was very brave because he didn't even recoil when I warned him about what Wimsey might do his clothing. I found out later that he was Trace Adkins. He's very nice man and he likes hounds. I'm a fan. Wimsey, meanwhile, continued to remain silent, obviously perplexed by all the activity that for once was not entirely focused on him. Fortunately our visit came to an end before he decided to do something about it.

We had no sooner returned to the holding area, however, than The Wimsey Tabernacle Choir was back in business. It was another ear-splitting, headache-inducing hour before I learned--with much relief--that the men had not chosen Wimsey. That honor went to the little bulldog puppy. Had Wimsey been chosen I am sure the agent would have thrown himself off the roof. And I'm not sure I wouldn't have joined him.

"How did it go," Maria asked when I at last restored Wimsey to his rightful place digging his joints into her lap.

"Did you know that Wimsey can bay for eight straight hours with virtually no break?" I asked.

"Not specifically, no," she replied.

"Well that's how it went."

CHAPTER 20--HOLY HOUND

In light of the fact that I had so far failed abysmally to influence Wimsey's behavior using conventional methods, I thought that perhaps appealing to a Higher Power might yield better results.

"The Feast of St. Francis is coming up," I said to Maria. "What do you think about taking Wimsey to one of the Blessing of the Animals services?" She had heard my stories of how these services always seemed to have a calming effect on even the most rambunctious of shelter dogs.

"Do you really think it will help?" she asked dubiously.

"Well it could at least keep him out of the vet's office for a week," I replied.

Our initial plan was to bring Wimsey to a local church. But then I remembered that churches generally have excellent acoustics. The obvious alternative was to bring him to the Cathedral of St. John the Divine, the seat of Episcopal worship in New York City, which offered outdoor blessings. And while it was not impossible that Wimsey would somehow manage to get us kicked out, it did at least diminish the odds.

The Cathedral was a couple of miles uptown and since Wimsey was currently in the throes of a seasonal affliction known as The Fall Friskies, we were hoping that the pre-blessing walk might take the edge off it. It did exactly the opposite. Our route took us through a new neighborhood and Wimsey found the virgin sniffing territory so exhilarating that his Halti had to make its appearance well before we were even anywhere near our destination. And while the Halti might have enabled me to keep my feet on the ground it did absolutely nothing to deter Wimsey from charging into the Cathedral Close to broadcast the news of his arrival in the loudest possible terms.

"Is it working yet?" Maria asked.

And if Wimsey's deportment wasn't exactly the serene and meditative aspect I had hoped for it certainly wasn't helped by all the activity going on around us. The Close looked like a cross between a circus and a medieval fair. There were rows of gaily decked out tables and booths selling all kinds of merchandise, there were displays and exhibits showcasing all kinds of animals and there were people strolling everywhere with all kinds of pets. What there weren't were priests. Our arrival had coincided with a clerical lunch break.

"So much for a quick and quiet blessing," I observed to Maria.

But if we were disappointed, Wimsey was delighted. He scarcely knew in which direction to drag me first. He beelined over to an exhibit of farm animals and began to contemplate its donkey like an art historian with a Renaissance masterpiece. And such was the level of his interest that it took our combined efforts to prevent him from conducting a much closer investigation than was good for either animal.

"When did you say those priests are getting back?" Maria asked as soon as the donkey was out of harm's way, a circumstance to which Wimsey, if not the donkey, objected strenuously.

"I didn't, but anyway I need photos for this week's blog post."

Tormenting Wimsey with the camera had become a weekly blogging chore and I was always on the lookout for new and appealing photo opportunities. But so far these seemed to consist largely of Wimsey baying, towing, inserting his nose into the backsides of the other blessees or drooling hungrily at the members of the Birds of Prey Exhibit. And when he was not engaging in behaviors of which St. Francis was unlikely to approve, he was trying to remove his Halti by smearing his face on people's pants or else trying to lift his leg on ornamental shrubbery. And if Wimsey was loud when he was bored, when he was both bored and thwarted he was even louder. People from around the grounds came to see what was happening and we fielded the usual questions.

"Why is he baying?"

"Because we don't want him to."

"Can you make him stop?"

"We can't make him stop doing anything."

"Can he bay on command?"

"He does nothing on command."

"Does he find lost people?"

"Only if they get lost while eating lunch."

"Do bloodhounds make good pets?"

Our combined "No!" might even have been louder than Wimsey's baying.

When we were finally able to tear Wimsey away from his admirers and foil his attempts to cavort with farm animals, we decided to pass the time by taking a look at the tables of merchandise. Wimsey was just in the process of smearing his face along the side of a table selling religious books when a woman approached the table. She leaned over and spoke quietly to the book seller.

"The Bishop is going to be coming out of the side exit at 2 o'clock," she murmured. It was obvious why she didn't want anyone to overhear. Bishops are the rock stars of the Cathedral Close and his appearance was likely to draw crowds even larger than Wimsey's.

It gave me an idea. I motioned to Maria.

"Here, take the camera," I said. "Wimsey is going to ambush the Bishop." A picture of Wimsey with the Bishop might possibly even make up for all the other ones I had of him trying to trample the flower beds, sample the baked goods and annoy the other animals.

I dragged Wimsey away from the table and lurked near the site of the Bishop's egress as inconspicuously as it is possible to lurk while holding onto a 125-pound hound who is not a fan of lurking. I knew that if I had any hope of getting a picture I needed to get to the Bishop before anyone realized he was there.

My patience was rewarded. Promptly at 2 pm a side door opened and the Bishop quietly emerged. As soon as he cleared the gate I was on him.

"Bishop, would you mind taking a picture with my dog," I asked, noting with approval that the Bishop appeared to be a tall, sturdy-looking chap and unlikely to topple.

The Bishop looked a bit uncertain at this request. He probably assumed like many people we met that Wimsey's Halti was a muzzle. The irony was that of all Wimsey's body parts his mouth was the only one you never had to worry about. Not that Wimsey ever intended to hurt anyone with his body parts, it's just that he had a natural talent for it.

After a moment's hesitation, however, the Bishop gamely agreed. Perhaps he thought that given the occasion a refusal might show a want of faith. I quickly positioned Wimsey next to his pristine purple cassock and prayed that he wouldn't decide to use it as a napkin or to launch an investigation into what was under it. But whether it was the proximity of one of God's senior representatives, or more likely that I gave him too little time to exercise his imagination, he just stood there quietly. And although Wimsey was not looking at the camera—that really would have been a miracle—he was looking up at the Bishop in a way that suggested that they were in deep discussion of some fascinating ecclesiastical matter. Given that the fascinating ecclesiastical matter Wimsey wished to discuss probably had something to do with the fascinating ecclesiastical cassock, I thanked the Bishop profusely and moved Wimsey away before he was able to do anything about it. It was the first usable picture of the day.

"Look, the priests are back!" Maria said, pointing to a field where people and animals were lining up.

We joined the end of a line and Wimsey, obviously wanting to atone for his momentary lapse into exemplary behavior, immediately began trying to interfere with the tranquility of his neighbors. When I removed him out of nose-poking and paw-thwacking range, he alternated between baying at me angrily and rolling around on the grass and trying to remove his Halti.

By the time our turn with the priest came Wimsey was so loud, annoyed and grass stained that if he looked any more unworshipful he would have had horns and a pitchfork. The priest took one look at him and the grass filled slingers that dangled from his mouth and stood well back and at arm's length to administer the blessing. As soon as it was over, I hustled Wimsey away before he could either bay at the poor man or decorate his snowy white cassock with green-tinted flingage.

We headed to the exit and as we left it was apparent that the same loud and uncooperative dog who had dragged me into the Cathedral Close was the same loud and uncooperative dog who was dragging me out of it.

"I don't think it worked," Maria said as Wimsey began baying at a traffic light.

Our quick pilgrimage had taken us four and a half hours.

As soon as we were back at Maria's apartment, Wimsey dove face first into a large bowl of turkey and kibble, sucked up the contents of his water bowl and then climbed onto Maria's bed for a satisfying snore and fart-filled nap.

Wimsey was truly blessed. Us not so much.

CHAPTER 21--MISCELLANEOUS MEDIA MATTERS

Wimsey may not have been the judge's favorite hound (at least not so far), but it was a different story entirely over at Running Paws, the dog running service that provided him with a daily romp in Central Park. It was a love-fest all around. Maria loved Running Paws and the theoretical Wimsey-taming exercise the service provided, (although in truth I failed to find much evidence of this), Running Paws loved Maria for the enthusiastic references she gave to prospective clients and Wimsey absolutely adored his Running Paws runners, a feeling they inexplicably reciprocated in spite of the fact that they stared death in the face every time they picked up his leash.

Wimsey's favorite runner was undoubtedly Roy, who Maria and I nicknamed Braveheart, since although unquestionably fit, he was not a big man. What was even more remarkable, was that he often ran Wimsey in tandem with an oversized and energetic Weimaraner named Louie. How Roy managed to survive the experience was a frequent cause for speculation.

As per the company's protocol, Roy left a daily note on the status of Wimsey's eliminatory activities, a missive that he often embellished with brief and cryptic observations such as, "Wimsey was quite excited today," or 'Wimsey was quite playful today" or "Wimsey really enjoyed himself today" and although the exact form any of this took was never specified, usually when Wimsey was excited, playful and enjoying himself, no one else was.

Roy also had a terrific sense of humor (you would have to, to enjoy spending time with Wimsey) and one day he sent us this which provided some further illumination:

Notes I Wanted to Leave But Never Did

"Today Wimsey almost killed me going down the stairs." (This would be a recurring note, actually).
"Today Wimsey decided to poo in/on/through the railing around a tree. I think he was challenging me."

"Wimsey tried to drag me into oncoming traffic today. On purpose?"

"Today Wimsey pooped a poop bigger than my head."

"Wimsey and Louie decided to have a race back home from the park, and we almost killed one old man, two nice ladies taking a walk, a Boston terrier, and three policemen, ON YOUR LEFT! ON YOURRR LEFT!!!"

"Wimsey was in the mood for sprints today: he'd run full speed for fifty feet, then jerk me to a dead stop so he could sniff some pee for five minutes, then bolt off another fifty feet, then jerk to a stop... and so on, all the way through the park."

"I think Wimsey accidentally inhaled a Chihuahua."

"Wimsey is the best dog in the world, and while it's true that he's slobbery, bossy, stubborn, and stinky, it's also true that he's handsome, proud, and awesome and loads of fun. Nothing beats running full tilt through a gaggle of Japanese tourists behind 125 pounds of jowl-flapping bloodhound."

Cheers!
Roy

I found it oddly reassuring that Maria and I weren't the only victims of Wimsey's flamboyant walking style—it was a miracle that it didn't send any of us to the hospital on a regular basis. One minute you were happily zipping along and the next you went flying over his midsection because he had screeched to a sudden halt and pivoted directly in front of you. We called it The Pommel Horse. Equally disconcerting was when he did an abrupt about face and lunged at a spot behind you to sniff something he had missed. Its effect on your shoulder was varying degrees of excruciating depending on how interesting the spot.

Given that Wimsey wasn't exactly the easiest animal to walk, Maria and I were surprised by a call she received one day from the owner of Running Paws.

"Hi Maria. It's Seth. I'm calling because *The New York Times* is going to do a story on us and they want to send a photographer out with one of our runners. We thought that Roy, Louie and Wimsey would make a compelling visual. Is that OK?"

Maria readily agreed although we thought it made a compelling visual just to see Roy make it down the street intact. It was certainly a ringing endorsement of their runners.

The article appeared a week later.

"That's so him!" Maria exclaimed when she saw the picture.

It was fair to say that the photographer had captured the spirit of the enterprise perfectly. He caught the trio barreling along in mid-stride. Roy is looking straight ahead. Louie is looking straight ahead. And Wimsey? Wimsey is looking straight into the camera. And with a very familiar expression on his face.

"He definitely knows who you should be looking at," Maria continued.

While this was undoubtedly true, I knew that Wimsey wasn't looking at the camera. He was looking at the guy holding the camera. He wanted turkey.

Wimsey's next media outing began very differently, however.

In December Maria handed me an envelope.

"Merry Christmas!" she said with a big grin. Inside wasn't a present but a lump of coal. It was a letter conveying the news that Wimsey would once again be gracing the green carpets of The Westminster Kennel Club Dog Show. Only this time he would be dragging me along with him.

A few weeks later my phone rang.

"Hi Elizabeth. It's Daisy." Daisy was a friend who lived around the corner and worked for the American Kennel Club's communications department. She was also one of Wimsey's biggest fans as was Olive, her exquisite little 13-inch beagle with whom Wimsey was persistently smitten.

"The AKC is going to hold a pre-Westminster "Meet the Breeds" press event at the Affinia Hotel," she said, "and we'd like Wimsey to attend if he's free."

"Yes, we'd love to attend," I said. If there was a canine equivalent of a stage Mom, I was it.

"Great!" she said. Then she continued, "Originally we were going to have Wimsey lead a parade of dogs over to Madison Square Garden, but there isn't going to be time, unfortunately."

It was a good thing there wasn't. It wouldn't have been much of a parade if it had to stop every five feet so Wimsey could lift his leg on something he wasn't supposed to lift his leg on. Or if he tried to lead from the rear. In more ways than one.

"Oh, also, I want to take Wimsey on a live morning TV show the day after," she added.

I called Maria.

"No!" was the first thing out of her mouth. "Is Daisy insane!" was the second. "You cannot let her take Wimsey on live TV. She'll get fired."

But before I could call Daisy, she called me.

"I'm so sorry, Elizabeth, my boss vetoed Wimsey. He wants me to take a smaller dog." Or perhaps, I thought to myself, one who wouldn't bay over people trying to talk or fling drool at the camera or drag her out of her chair to investigate some interesting scent or try to assassinate the fuzzy microphone boom. And that's just the stuff I knew he would do.

She was so apologetic that I didn't have the heart to tell her just how big a bullet she had dodged.

But there was still the press event to get through and when Wimsey and I arrived at The Affinia we were greeted by a woman with a stack of AKC jackets of all different sizes. They were all too small. I sighed. Everything always was, whether it was coats, couches, laps, bottles of shampoo or pizzas. None of this was helped by the fact that Wimsey's nose had detected something extremely interesting going on in the nearby ballroom and he was growing increasingly insistent about investigating it.

We finally just threw an XL jacket over his head— the largest one they had and left the closures open. By this time Wimsey was in a frenzied state of anticipation and ignoring the fact that I had rolled up his leash to its shortest extent, he hurtled into the ballroom like a guided missile and announced himself in a voice that I was certain could be heard several floors above. The reason for his excitement was obvious. The place was throbbing with activity. Not only were there a substantial number of purebred dogs and handlers walking around but there were also two large exhibitions underway with crowds of reporters and cameramen all jostling to get a better view.

The first was an agility demonstration that featured a pack of off-leash border collies all of whom were manically jumping over rails, weaving through poles, charging through tunnels, running up and down A-frames and performing other impressive feats of canine athleticism. The second exhibition, although more sedate, also had a pack of off leash dogs. In this case, Golden Retrievers, who were demonstrating impressive feats of canine obedience. They were all so calm, waggy and eager to please that it was hard not to find them endearing. Wimsey certainly did. He took one look at them and all the other fast moving, free range canines and went berserk. If the AKC had wanted an exhibition of furious baying and dragging, they definitely had one. I deeply regretted my decision not to use a Halti or Gentle Leader because of the muzzle-like optics, but I reminded myself that the event was called "Meet the Breeds" and not "Meet the Good Breeds."

Even with everything else going on around us, however, it was hard to ignore what was going on in the corner into which I had corralled Wimsey. His attempts to join the games of chase he saw at the other end of the room were growing increasingly vigorous and vociferous. A reporter from *The New York Post* came over to see what all the commotion was about. Perhaps he had gotten bored with watching dogs who were actually listening to their handlers. Whatever the reason, as soon as he saw Wimsey his face lit up with an admiration I had often seen on the faces of men. Leaving aside their obvious appreciation of Wimsey's fine and very visible set of testicles, men sensed in Wimsey a kindred spirit---he had challenging personal hygiene issues, he was messy, loud, opinionated and self-centered, he was stubbornly committed to getting his way, he snored, was unapologetically flatulent and was disinclined to listen to the woman he lived with. That's not to say that Wimsey wasn't equally popular with the ladies, just for different reasons. They thought he was insanely cute. He was also charming, handsome and a nightmare to live with—in fact every woman's bad boyfriend. They loved him.

"Wow, now that's a real dog!" declared Wimsey's latest media conquest. Unfortunately at the moment Wimsey was all too real. We were engaged in a spirited contest of tug of war in which the consequences of losing would be far more disruptive than just being dragged over a line. As I leaned backwards at a precarious angle to keep Wimsey from joining his more active brethren, the reporter peppered me with questions. We had to scream at each other over the sound of Wimsey's protests, periodically punctuated by my ineffectual cries of "Wimsey, no!" And when *The Post's* photographer arrived to take Wimsey's picture, Garbo herself couldn't have done a better job of taking personal offense to the camera.

When I spoke to Maria after the event I warned her not to expect much in the way of media coverage. But the next day when I opened *The Post* I was both surprised and gratified. Their coverage of the event led with a prominently displayed picture of Wimsey—probably taken in a millisecond between bays—and an account of his life in New York City. I noted with satisfaction that the agility and obedience dogs had been relegated to the second page. Also that their picture was smaller.

Maria, however, was not surprised.

"Bad boys rule," she proclaimed.

Too bad not in the show ring.

CHAPTER 22--A STAR PUPIL

With Westminster fast approaching, I asked Maria to video my trotting practice sessions with Wimsey. He looked fine. Me not so much. I galloped around looking like a cross between Groucho Marx and The Leaning Tower of Pisa. I hadn't actually known it was possible to run tilted both forwards and sideways at the same time.

"I think I need another handling class," I said to Maria.

Fortunately the therapy dog instructor at the ASPCA knew of a group class in New Jersey that had immediate availability. The class was being held at a canine training center about an hour outside of Manhattan so we once again borrowed Ray's car and since the GPS and I had very different interpretations of the meaning of "keep right," we were also the last to arrive.

I replaced Wimsey's prong with his show lead, took a very deep breath and let him out of the car. He wasted no time in dragging me across the parking lot, through the doors of the building and into a large, gym-like room against one wall of which there lounged an assortment of unusually handsome purebred dogs of all different sizes and breeds. Their handlers were an equally diverse lot and even included a few children who were not much bigger than the dogs they were expected to handle.

But before we could join them we had to make our way through a crowd of friends and family who had assembled to watch. Wimsey, clearly believing that they were all there to see him, cut a swathe through their midst and proceeded to greet everyone like the guest of honor at a surprise party. When we finally made it out the other side—after a few squeals of delight and otherwise— Wimsey was just in the process of repeating his performance with his fellow classmates when he suddenly stopped, rammed his ears forward and looked around like he had lost something. His nose twitched in the direction of the crowd and when it had locked itself onto Maria's scent he began to trumpet at her like a bull elephant. I stuffed a large piece of chicken into his mouth but he continued to stare fixedly at her while he chewed. She tried to hide behind a tall man. He trumpeted. She slid out the door. He trumpeted even louder.

I was just wondering how long my supply of chicken and liver would last when Gina, our instructor, strode to the center of the room. Wimsey, momentarily distracted by the presence of a new human, turned his attention to analyzing her scent while she issued her instructions.

"Let's start by taking the group once around the ring," she said. "I don't want any of you to carry bait in your hands. We want the dogs looking straight ahead, not at your hand."

Several of my show books had recommended the same thing but Wimsey was not a fan of this system. He was fundamentally a transactional animal, something my repeated use of positive reinforcement had unfortunately positively reinforced. And like any good businessman dealing with a shady character he also demanded to inspect my proposed method of payment to make sure it was of a form he was willing to accept. He stared at my empty hand with a "no meat, no move" expression written all over his face.

I caved and extracted a piece of chicken. The chicken proved acceptable. So much so in fact that he swung his body perpendicular to mine and pranced and danced sideways with a mincing vine step. Toss in some baying and head shaking and he resembled a singing, dancing, drool-flinging crab. Hoping to shut down his crustacean imitation, I put the chicken in front of his nose to get him facing forward. It worked but he chased my outstretched arm around the ring at a gallop.

Things didn't really improve much from there. Whenever it was our turn to go around the ring alone, I did my best not to look like Groucho Marx while Wimsey did his best not to look like a show dog. He either paced, tropped, galloped or refused to move at all depending on where I held the chicken or liver. When I tried to stack him he stack danced and when I tried to free stack him he stalked stacked. And in between he stared at Maria and bayed. Even the dogs handled by children looked better.

When class was over, Gina took me aside.

"I think perhaps you need to do a better job entertaining Wimsey so he won't get so bored. Try playing with him while you wait." Her face had the same look on it as my previous instructor's when she watched me try to move Wimsey's legs.

"And the chicken and liver you are using are good but try cooking him some London broil to add variety."

I'm sure Wimsey wondered if she could come live with us.

"Look, he's not easy dog but if you practice a lot, you'll do fine," she added.

I found this encouraging since I, too, believed that with enough effort I would (eventually) prevail. I conveniently ignored the fact that Wimsey was a dog who had trained me to retrieve his bone when he threw it off the bed, to serve him water from fountains with the portable bowl that I purchased for that purpose, to feed him a rotating Snack of the Day when he poked my pouch like it was a Pez dispenser, to cut his food into bite-sized sized pieces, to put the correct amount of mayonnaise in his tuna fish and to change his water when there was too much drool in it.

It was clear that Wimsey knew quite a bit about the principles of training. I just needed to reverse the process.

CHAPTER 23--DOWN BY THE BOARDWALK

If I was unable to secure Wimsey's cooperation in the show ring I was absolutely determined that it wouldn't be for want of trying. We decided to enter him in a large indoor show being held the Saturday before Westminster in Cape May, New Jersey. Since we had an early ring time it meant an overnight stay and preparing for it was more like we were mounting an expedition to Borneo rather than one to the Jersey Shore. Wimsey had so much stuff that it took several color-coded Excel spread sheets to keep track of it all and the skills of a Euclidian scholar to fit it all into Ray's diminutive SUV. And anything that didn't fit in the back--like the two fully loaded bags of food from Fairway I brought in case New Jersey ran out--ended up on Maria's lap. Even stashing Wimsey was a tight squeeze. He barely had room enough to admire himself in the rear-view mirror or to snuffle my bare neck whenever I least expected it.

By the time we arrived at the hotel it was already dark which meant that we were able install Wimsey when no one could see him. It was much safer that way. I was anxious that although the hotel was supposed to be pet friendly this might not include pets the size of miniature horses who dripped drool and dispensed fur like a flower girl at a wedding. We probably had more cleaning supplies with us than the housekeeper.

Our room was a ground floor one-bedroom suite and as soon as we had unpacked and Wimsey had thoroughly familiarized himself with its amenities we leashed him up to explore our new surroundings. Neither of us had ever been to Cape May before and it seemed to be a delightful place with rows of quaint Victorian houses that oozed picturesque charm. What it did not ooze was people. Cape May was a summer resort and in the dead of winter it looked like it had been recently visited by an apocalypse of a fairly major kind.

Maria looked around nervously.

"Where are all the people?" she asked. For New Yorkers like us their absence was definitely creepy and disconcerting.

"I don't know. Maybe Wimsey is trying to find them," I said as he dragged me through the dimly-lit streets like he had an appointment for which he was disinclined to be late.

"I wonder where he thinks he's going?" she asked uneasily.

"I just hope it's not anywhere with decomposing bodies and men in Hazmat suits," I replied.

Maria looked around again.

"It's like we're the last two people on earth….with Wimsey."

I shuddered at the thought. As much as we loved him, Wimsey's presence in such a situation would definitely be less than optimal.

Wimsey didn't manage to find any people, but after an hour of diligent searching he did manage to find an acceptable spot for one of his large and fragrant deposits. He was as finicky about what came out of him as he was about what went into him. We decided to call it a night.

Since Maria wasn't going to be the one ring wrestling Wimsey in the morning, we had agreed that I would take the bedroom and she would sleep on the sofa bed in the living room.

"Come here and feel this mattress," she said after she had opened it. I felt it. While not exactly a bed of nails it was definitely a bed of lumps. Wimsey obviously thought so too. He climbed up, climbed down, and then took himself off down the long hallway to find more acceptable accommodation. Which happened to be my bed.

We were surprised. We had both assumed that Wimsey would spend the night in the corridor between our rooms since it offered him the best vantage point from which to surveil us in case one of us tried to escape. And although the nighttime sharing of a bed was generally anathema to him, tonight he obviously decided to make an exception. Probably because I didn't want him to. The nap we had taken together had left a lasting impression. I tried to lure him off the bed with some turkey but unfortunately the possum prevailed and when I returned from brushing my teeth I saw that he had stretched himself out the wide way across the king-sized bed and was snoring loudly. It was not a restful night.

Nor was the next morning which was a whirl of frenzied activity. Getting the three of us groomed (two of us needing extra time because we looked like racoons) and the car loaded with Wimsey's giant crate plus his food, our food and show paraphernalia was not an easy or quick task. Fortunately, according to the GPS the Wildwood Convention Center was a quick twenty-minute drive away. We made it forty-five. Wimsey meanwhile passed the time dancing around in the back seat like he was going to another J. Crew shoot or to a show dog class in which he would be fed an assortment of fine meats that he did as little as possible to deserve.

Our late arrival meant that when I was finally able to find a parking spot, it was located at a considerable distance from the main entrance. As we debated the best way to get Wimsey and his numerous chattels into the building in one trip he bounced around in the bracing sea air in a way that did not bode well for our efforts. I put him in his Halti and when we had finally managed to push, pull haul and wrangle our way over to the main entrance I noticed a tall, stern-looking, white-haired woman wearing a judge's badge standing in front of the door. She was staring at Wimsey, his Halti or both. Perhaps Haltis weren't permitted at the show but even if they were, you could make the argument that if your dog needed one as badly as Wimsey very obviously needed his, then perhaps you shouldn't be showing it. The judge's face made that argument.

She stepped aside to allow us to pass and what we found inside was sheer bedlam. The space was enormous and all of it seemed to be a heaving sea of crates, grooming tables, equipment, show rings, people, and of course dogs. Everyone seemed to be either shouting or barking. Wimsey took one look and tucked his tail firmly underneath him.

We found a small unoccupied spot next to a grooming table and wedged Wimsey's crate into it.

"Let's put him into his crate," I suggested. "Maybe it will help him get acclimated. In the meantime I'm going to go get changed."

I was particularly eager to debut the new outfit I had purchased especially for Westminster. I was hoping to make quite a splash in it. It consisted of a green suede jacket, green trousers, green shoes, green socks and a green spit rag. They were all in a shade that we called Wimsey Green because it brought out the rich red of Wimsey's mahogany coat. The only thing that wasn't green was a cream-colored silk blouse with pearl buttons.

When I returned, Maria looked me up and down.

"That's a lot of green," she observed. I thought I looked elegant, she thought I looked like a leprechaun.

But my outfit wasn't the only thing that was new. The show marked a series of firsts. It was our first indoor show, the first time Wimsey would be the only bloodhound in the ring which also meant that it would be the first time I would be handed a Best of Breed ribbon (barring it being the first time he found a way to get himself disqualified) and it would be the first time I would get to show Wimsey in the Hound Group. I was excited.

As our ring time approached, Maria extracted Wimsey from his crate and I slipped his show lead over his head. His tail unfurled. The lead promptly disappeared into dewlap and Wimsey promptly tried to disappear somewhere that wasn't a show ring. Maria blocked him from one side, I blocked him from the other and together we herded him over to the bloodhound ring like a pair of over-zealous border collies.

When we arrived I saw a familiar figure inside the ring watching us. It was the judgmental judge from our arrival.

"Arggh, it would be her!" I hissed to Maria.

'Yes, but she has to give him Best of Breed. He's the only bloodhound."

I shrugged, grabbed a fistful of Wimsey and pulled him into the ring. As I began trying to stack him, the judge scowled at me. Whether this was due to the epic battle underway with Wimsey's feet or something else, I had no idea. You really didn't need a reason to scowl at me when I was trying to show Wimsey.

"Over here, please," she snapped.

"Oh, was I supposed to stack him in front of you?" I asked sheepishly. Since I had never shown Wimsey as a solo dog before it hadn't occurred to me to bring him up immediately for his examination.

"You are supposed to present your dog to the judge," she said with a withering look that reminded me of the one my riding teachers gave me when I was cantering on the wrong lead. I prodded Wimsey over to the spot in front of her but this time she didn't even bother to wait for me to entangle myself with his feet.

"Down and back," she commanded.

Maria had been standing ringside to offer moral support but now Wimsey began to stare at her like she might vaporize if he ceased. He paced away from the judge looking backwards over his shoulder at Maria and then

paced back with his head angled sharply in her direction.
He free stacked in front of Maria instead of the judge.

"Do you want us to go once around?" I asked.

"That is usually what is done" (the "you idiot"
being implied), she said impatiently.

Wimsey moved forward but for once he was not
looking at the chicken in my hand. He absolutely refused to
let Maria out of his sight. All of this would have been
understandable if Wimsey was a devoted kind of a dog. But
he wasn't a devoted kind of a dog. He was the kind of a
dog who got peeved if Maria stayed home from work
because her presence disturbed his morning nap; he was the
kind of dog who pushed her aside so he could say hello to
me if we both walked through the door at the same time;
and he was the kind of a dog who made it abundantly clear
that if he had to choose between either of us and a piece of
organ meat, there would be no contest. Wimsey had many
fine qualities (although in truth I often struggled to find
them) but loyalty was not among them.

The judge sighed and grudgingly held out the Best of Breed ribbon. I grabbed it as Wimsey dragged me out of the ring, launched himself onto Maria and planted both paws on her shoulders and bellowed in her face like they had been parted for an eternity.

"Maybe you shouldn't be ringside," I said.

"Yes, but he'll smell me wherever I am," she replied. "I'll have to leave the building."

Unfortunately what neither of us realized was that instead of the groups being judged in parallel in different rings they were being judged sequentially in one ring. The result was that Maria got to enjoy a raw February sojourn at the seaside while I got to watch Wimsey take a three-hour nap.

Wimsey was considerably refreshed by his lengthy nap and when it came time to liberate him from his crate he shot out of it eager to see what was next up on the entertainment agenda. When he discovered that this involved socializing with the group of hounds assembling outside of the Group ring he was so delighted by the prospect that it took my surreptitious use of his Halti to get us there.

After some preliminary skirmishing with his fellow hounds it was time for the Hound Group to enter the ring. I took up a position behind a swift-looking coonhound, trusting to its footspeed to offer the greatest odds of keeping Wimsey's nose out of its bottom. In this I was successful. In preventing Wimsey from chasing it I was not. While we waited for the judge's examination Wimsey did his best to rectify his failure. Fortunately we were near the front of the line so our wait was not a long one. I tugged on Wimsey's lead. Wimsey demonstrated all the mobility of a cement block. As much as he enjoyed his cozy visits with the judge he apparently had no intention of abandoning all the heady scent of hound that swirled around him. My method of persuading him otherwise might easily have been mistaken for dragging had the judge been looking in our direction. Luckily the judge was still deeply immersed in the finer points of coonhound which also meant that I had plenty of time to wage war with Wimsey's feet. But remarkably, Wimsey appeared to have little interest in what was happening with his feet. The same could not be said for his interest in the line of hounds behind him, however. He spun his head around like the child in *The Exorcist* to watch them.

The judge came over and ran his hands over Wimsey, tactfully ignored his unconventional stance.

"Down and back, please."

I pulled out a piece of chicken and gave Wimsey a tug. Wimsey sniffed dismissively at the chicken and tried to rejoin his friends. Obviously it was time for the big guns. I took out a large piece of liver and waved it in front of his nose. Wimsey stared at the liver and took a breath of such suspicious depth that I had to shove the liver into his mouth to stop him from impressing the judge with the strength of his lungs. I was ultimately able to get him to move forward with a second piece of liver but he did so with such excruciating slowness that he appeared to be in imminent danger of falling asleep. All that changed, however, when we turned around. He took off at a gallop. He was heading straight towards the judge. Wimsey had never actually succeeded in body slamming a judge before but body slamming, like wrestling, was a popular sport in the Wimsey Olympics and now he was going for the Gold.

Wimsey's lead was once again buried deep in a crevasse of dewlap and the laws of momentum appeared to be all on his side. I dug my heels deep into the carpet and hauled backwards using all my weight. Wimsey did exactly the opposite using all of his. It was not a pretty sight. Nor was Wimsey's position when he screeched to a halt a hair's breadth away from the judge. The judge accorded him the most cursory of looks before moving on the next and certainly more promising candidate. There probably weren't any ribbons in our future but neither was there a judge with Wimsey sitting on his stomach.

I gaited Wimsey along the rail back to the end of the line at which point he sprang into a fluid, lively and wholly unobserved trot.

Incredibly, things went downhill from there. The fact that we had been at the front of the line before meant that we were at the back of it now. There were twenty-five other hounds to be examined and Wimsey thought traffic lights took too long. While I contemplated how to best occupy the time Wimsey came up with his own solution to the question. The dog directly behind us was a Norwegian Elkhound. Wimsey had never met a Norwegian Elkhound before. He wanted to. He began to strain forcefully in an elkhoundward direction.

"Wimsey, leave that elkhound alone!" I commanded, entirely for the benefit of its handler since I knew that Wimsey had absolutely no intention of leaving that elkhound alone.

My options at this point were limited. If I moved Wimsey forward, his nose would be up the coonhound's bottom; if I moved him back closer to the rail, he might mistake some spectator's trousers for a napkin; if I moved him deeper into the ring he would bay because I had moved him away from the other hounds.

Then I remembered Gina's suggestion that I should entertain him. I began an extensive and chirpy dialog, the purport of which was the bald-faced lie that he was a good boy. Wimsey had absolutely no interest in my opinion as to his goodness and considerable interest in improving his knowledge of fluffy hound breeds.

If entertaining him wasn't working maybe annoying him would. He hated being stacked. I stacked him. At least thwarting me gave him something rewarding to do that did not involve pouncing on the elkhound, baying, getting overly personal with the spectators or eating liver and belching and farting liver fumes.

It is astonishing how long and scary an hour can be when you are attached by a slender strap to a dog that is very large, very energetic and extremely bored. I don't recommend it. When the judge at long last called for the final group once around, Wimsey finished up in the style in which he began— his body pointed forward and his head pointed backward. He very much enjoyed watching the elkhound go once around.

We didn't win.

When Maria found us afterwards, she started to make a fuss over Wimsey.

"Don't you dare be nice to him!" I cried. Then I brought her up to speed on the last few hours in graphic detail and with very unladylike language. She listened while she tried not to pass out from a combination of hunger and hypothermia.

It was unclear which of us had the worse day.

CHAPTER 24--WESTMINSTER TAKE THREE

We returned to New York on Saturday evening and Wimsey took up residence in my apartment for the remainder of his pre-Westminster preparations. These included a large number of intensive cavaletti sessions on Sunday which ended up being more for my benefit than his since he seemed to regard them purely as an opportunity to engage in some advanced snacking.

I didn't get much sleep that night. Between my excitement and the sound of Wimsey's nails sculpting sleeping quarters in the comforter I put on the floor because I thought it would be quieter than his nails digging into the carpet, I was awake for most of it. When the alarm went off at 5:30 sharp, Wimsey was still fast asleep, no doubt exhausted from his many architectural endeavors the night before. But as soon as I crawled out of bed to suit up for the frigid conditions outside Wimsey crawled into it and onto my spot where I found him snoring blissfully on top of my duvet. I rattled his collar and leash and prattled on like an overly caffeinated morning talk show host about how much fun it would be to leave his warm bed and take a freezing walk in the Arctic. Wimsey was not impressed. He opened one red-rimmed eye, took one look at his collar and leash and slammed it shut it again, being sure to add an extra decibel level to the snoring in case I was obtuse enough to have missed the point. It took an entire bag of turkey to get him out the door.

When we returned from our frosty walk Wimsey tucked into a sustaining breakfast of scrambled eggs, turkey, rice, yam and kibble while I tried not to throw up from nerves. Fortunately I had little time to think. We were soon out the door again, into a Pet Chauffeur taxi and speeding down the quiet and cold streets of Manhattan to Madison Square Garden. We arrived to find Beverly from the ASPCA already there waiting for us. I had asked her to be my assistant handler for the day since Maria had decided to absent herself entirely from Wimsey's orbit lest her presence trigger another one of his devoted dog impersonations. I had also particularly wanted Beverly's help because in addition to being the ASPCA's Volunteer Coordinator she was also an accomplished dog trainer and possessed a singular talent for playfully riling up her charges that I thought would help Wimsey relax.

Given Wimsey's two prior performances at Westminster my goals for this one were extremely modest. If I could get him to trot and not tuck his tail and to look as much like Wimsey without actually acting as much like Wimsey, I would consider the show a roaring success. I just hoped that my childhood dream of showing a dog at Westminster didn't end up with me face first in green carpet.

As ring time approached I gave Wimsey one last rub with the chamois cloth and we began the arduous task of trying to fight our way through the dense two-way traffic of dogs, handlers and spectators all of whom were either trying to get to or from the rings at the same time. We made slow progress and Wimsey began to look a bit overwhelmed. But happily (or not) as soon as we arrived ringside he settled down to evaluate the social possibilities of his situation and to let me know how he felt about them. He began with a few squeaks, escalated to mini-bays and then inhaled deeply preparatory to what was almost certainly going to be a bay of thunderously embarrassing proportions. But suddenly, just as he opened his mouth a large stuffed lamb came flying out of nowhere and inserted itself adroitly into it. Beverly! She played a ferocious game of tug of war with him and when he grew bored with the lamb she fed him cookies and wrestled with him. She talked, prodded and cajoled. Wimsey's tail definitely wasn't tucked, but I wasn't sure that I liked the alternative all that much either.

Wimsey was probably even more annoyed than usual when our number was called and he had to enter the ring. I waited as long as I could to maximize the space between him and the dog in front of us and then I took off like Usain Bolt off the blocks. Wimsey shot out beside me like a racing greyhound chasing a rabbit. He executed two electrifying gallop strides and then fell back into a trot. Yes an actual trot! I felt like we had just won Best in Show. I surged with pride.

The effect of all the riling up, however, made itself felt as soon as I tried to stack him. Every time he saw me even reach for one for his legs, he withdrew it preemptively. As the judge moved down the line I stood up and tried not to notice that Wimsey's inside rear leg jutted into the ring like he was doing the hokey-pokey.

While we waited for our turn with the judge, I tried to do my best Beverly imitation, especially since the fragrant fannies of the lady hounds were in dangerous proximity. But rather than trying to publicly sire a litter or entertain the crowd with his acoustic talents Wimsey turned his attention to the many bulges of bait that protruded from all my pockets. He began to poke at them in quick succession like they were buttons on a video game. By the time it was our turn for the judge's examination my Wimsey Green outfit was covered with Wimsey wet splotches.

I moved Wimsey into position and hoped the judge wouldn't notice that I looked like I had failed to find the lavatory in time. As I began trying to stack him, I was relieved to see that Wimsey now allowed me to touch his legs. Unfortunately he also now waited patiently until I was satisfied with their position before he moved them back to where they had been in the first place. The judge watched as Wimsey and I re-enacted The Myth of Sisyphus show dog style.

"Sometimes you just don't have enough hands," she opined sympathetically in a gracious southern drawl. I didn't think the problem was so much a shortage of hands as a surfeit of feet. All of them Wimsey's.

"Down and back please," she said, finally putting an end to the shenanigans.

I hoped we could redeem ourselves.

And redeem ourselves we did! For reasons known only to Wimsey, he once again decided to trot. Perhaps he liked the shock value. I was so happy and amazed that for once I didn't even care that his free stack looked like he was carrying out advanced tactical operations on a squirrel. At least he had stopped. As we made our way back to the end of the line Wimsey trotted thrillingly beside me. He looked like a normal show dog. Not a good one, mind, but definitely one within acceptable parameters. His tail was up. He was trotting. He didn't bay or try to wipe himself on the judge or attempt a love connection with the lady hounds. It was a Westminster triumph!

As expected, we didn't win any ribbons and although we weren't exactly covered in glory we weren't covered in disgrace either. I shook Beverly's hand when we exited the ring and Wimsey was so pleased to see her that he knee capped several people in the process. But then suddenly he stopped in mid-smack, sniffed the air and exploded in a series of greeting bays directed at the dense crowds streaming out of the stands. The bloodhound nose is truly a remarkable thing and when the crowds eventually parted I saw whose scent it was that Wimsey had detected. It was my friend Julie, a vet at the ASPCA. Wimsey had loved her from the first moment they met and she sat on him and tried unsuccessfully to cut his nails.

"You looked fabulous!" she gushed. "That's such a great outfit. It was the nicest one."

I made a mental note to review the purpose of a dog show with Julie.

While she critiqued the finer points of my outfit--minus the splotches--Wimsey alternated between baying at her, smearing her with slime, and converting the color of her clothing to his. Had space permitted, he most certainly would have stood on his head for her. He was ecstatic. The pointless ring stuff was over, he had "found" one of his favorite people, he was wearing a string around his neck, he had eaten an entire cow's worth of liver, and the lady who caused stuffed lambies to appear out of the ether was by his side. And with every step he was accosted by ardent admirers who having heard the sound of his voice, were eager to meet the celestial being from whom it emanated. So many people petted him that it was a wonder that he still had any hair left to shed on them.

But Wimsey's world was complete when he found Maria standing next to his crate. He sat on her, bayed at her, belched liver fumes at her, slimed her and then retired happily to his crate for a well-earned nap. The respite allowed Maria to turn her attention to giving interviews to the press, who as usual were to be found anywhere Wimsey was.

"What made you choose a bloodhound?" a reporter from *The Daily News* asked. Before Maria could reply a woman standing in front of the adjacent crate piped up,

"Insanity!" she cried.

The reporter probably thought she was joking. We knew she wasn't. This was how we met Karen, a bloodhound breeder whose hound Phoebe had just won an Award of Merit. And the judge wasn't the only one smitten by Phoebe's good looks. As soon as Wimsey woke up he began singing lovesick paeans to her beauty that prompted Karen to liberate its object from her crate. I did likewise with Wimsey--if for no other reason than to shut him up-- and he lost no time in jamming his cold, wet nose up Phoebe's backside by way of introduction.

"Watch out, Wimsey," Karen cautioned. "She lives with male bloodhounds and she will bite your nose." But Phoebe did not bite Wimsey's nose. She stood, gorgeous and regal and graciously allowed Wimsey's nose to have its unfettered way with her nether regions.

"Oooh," Karen exclaimed, "she likes him!"

"Ladies generally do," Maria responded. She was perhaps thinking of the well-endowed one in the low-cut blouse who had cradled Wimsey's head lovingly between her breasts. Or perhaps the festive ladies in front of a local tavern who had insisted that Wimsey keep the Santa hat he had stolen from one of them because he looked so cute with it. Or the woman we called Squeaky Lady who emitted ear piercing squeals whenever she saw him, or Pit Bull Lady who drew caricatures of him and fed him roast beef sandwiches, or Jewelry Lady or… it was a long list.

And the Wimsey lovefest continued at Westminster. By the time it was over, Maria and I were hoarse from answering questions.

"No, he didn't win,"

"Yes, you can have a bloodhound in Manhattan. What you can't have is a life."

"No, our apartments are small. He likes it that way so we can't escape from him."

"Yes he sheds. You learn to love black and tan."

"Yes he requires many hours of exercise. You won't need to diet."

"Yes, he eats a lot of food. Mostly yours."

"Yes he has a big bed. Mine."

"Is he eager to please you? No. He is eager for you to please him.

"Is he obedient? No."

"Is he a good dog? No."

"Is he ridiculous and entertaining? Yes."

We kept suggesting that people take a look at the Golden Retrievers instead.

I had such a good time that I didn't want it to end and it was close to midnight when I finally made my way back to my quiet and shockingly Wimsey-free apartment. Before I went upstairs I checked my mail. There was a letter in my mailbox.

It was for Wimsey.

Everything always was.

CHAPTER 25--MARCH MADNESS

After Westminster Maria and I decided that continuing to show Wimsey might be an enjoyable activity for all three of us. Wimsey liked to travel and we liked being a part of the bloodhound and show communities. And although Wimsey's deviations from the bloodhound breed standard made it unlikely that he would ever win anything, I still really wanted to see if I could persuade him to show with the same charismatic panache that he exhibited every day on the streets of New York. And we did seem to be on something of a roll in transforming Wimsey into a show ring specimen to be proud of instead of one to apologize for. He was obviously getting the hang of it.

A few weeks before our next show, I was telling my friend Sam, a well-known dog trainer in New York City, about Wimsey's issues in the ring.

"Well why don't you try an animal communicator," she suggested. "I can put you in touch with one and she can ask Wimsey if there is anything you can do to help him behave better."

At this point I was willing to try anything.

Mary, the animal communicator worked over the phone so I didn't need to bring Wimsey anywhere. At the start of our session she asked Wimsey's breed and age.

"Thanks. OK, there he is. I have him now. Wow, what an exceptional animal!" she enthused as she and Wimsey began to converse psychically. "He's one of the most intelligent dogs I have ever met."

As hard as it was for me to admit it, I was reluctantly forced to agree with her. I had recently become aware of the fact that in addition to being highly skilled in the training of humans, Wimsey could also do math.

Like so many of my other misguided attempts at training that had unintended consequences (The Tribute Couch comes to mind), the Door Snack was a prime example. Wimsey had ultimately agreed to forego the pleasure of being chased around my apartment with his collar and leash in exchange for a wad of turkey. But he had also decided that such an excellent principle deserved to be expanded upon. So although the wad of turkey allowed me to leash him up, it did not allow me to get him out the door. For that I needed to offer him an entirely different and even more special snack. His current favorite was a freeze-dried duck heart and in spite of the fact that it was small and Wimsey was big, he wouldn't touch it unless I cut it into quarters for him. The day before my talk with the communicator, the duck heart in question was a bit undersized and fearing that the quarters would be too small--and therefore grounds for rejection--I cut it into thirds. When he had finished them I opened the door. Wimsey didn't budge. And his body language made it clear that he had absolutely no intention of budging until he got his missing piece of duck heart. I had to forfeit a piece of salmon from that night's dinner to get him out the door. Wimsey knew how to count.

Astral Plane Wimsey was also apparently quite chatty.

"He's so talkative," Mary informed me as the session continued. "I can hardly get a word in edgewise." I observed Wimsey minutely for any evidence of this other worldly verbosity but if he was carrying on a conversation he was doing it while he snored.

"Did you ask him about the show ring?"

"I did. He says it's boring."

I think I had that one already figured out.

"Well ask him if there is anything I can do to make it less boring."

"He says no. Oh, wait a minute. He thinks maybe if you hopped up and down he might find it entertaining."

He probably wouldn't be the only one.

Our first show after Westminster was at the Westchester County Convention Center and this time not only did we have trouble finding the building but we couldn't find which of its many doors led to the dog show.

Wimsey probably had a pretty good idea of which door led to all the dogs but he also probably knew why we wanted to find it so he busied himself in conducting an exhaustive survey of the grounds. As we circled the Convention Center for perhaps the fifth time, I gave him a piece of cheese.

"Wimsey, find the dogs!" I commanded. He dragged me into a snowbank instead.

"How about this one?" Maria called out and pulled open a small, unobtrusive door at the rear of the property. Judging by the sound that hit us she had chosen correctly. The Convention Center had a basketball court and this one was so densely packed with dogs and rings that Wimsey's head spun around like a weathervane in a hurricane. And it continued to spin around in the breed bring where he was once again the only bloodhound.

"Maybe he's looking for a nice lady bloodhound," the judge suggested.

When was he not. And the lady in question didn't even have to be a bloodhound. Several months ago Wimsey had been spending the afternoon at my apartment when he began exhibiting some bizarre and alarming symptoms. He rushed to the door, clawed at it frantically and emitted an unearthly wail like nothing I had ever heard before. I naturally took this to mean that something of a messy gastrointestinal nature was about to manifest itself all over my floor so I lost no time in getting him outside. But rather than racing to the curb and producing a Niagara Falls of diarrhea, he dragged me across the street, pressed his nose to the pavement so firmly that it looked like it belonged to a pig and snorted his way methodically back and forth over the same stretch of sidewalk between 72nd and 73rd streets. Fifteen puzzling and non-productive minutes later, I took him back upstairs. But instead of checking his bowl for a delivery from the Food Fairy or inventorying his toy pile to make sure nothing had been played with or removed by an alien dog in his absence, he returned to his post wailing by the door. I leashed him up and took him outside again but he did exactly the same thing. I was mystified.

The next day I happened to run into a neighbor who owned Tango, a retired show Brittany and one of Wimsey's favorite lady sniffees.

"Where's Tango today?" I asked.

"Oh she's in heat, so I'm limiting her walks," he replied.

"Let me guess," I said. "You walk her across the street on Riverside between 72nd and 73rd?"

"Yes," he replied with surprise. Case closed.

Wimsey wasn't wailing, but he was behaving like he was surrounded by a sea of Tangos. Nevertheless we were still able to collect a Best of Breed ribbon and as we headed over to the Hound Group ring Maria stationed herself outside of it. Her days of exile were over. There seemed to be little point since it wasn't as if Wimsey was going to keep his head straight anyway and if the worst thing he did was stare at her, it would be an improvement.

We were just nearing the entrance to the ring when suddenly Wimsey's head plummeted to the ground like a pelican diving for a fish. His nose was pressed against a single, unremarkable-looking spot and he was snorting wildly. I tried to drag him away but since his show lead was just as effective in getting him to move as it was in getting him to stop, it didn't even look like I was going to be able to get him into to the ring at all.

I took out a piece of liver and jammed it between his nose and whatever probable lady scent he was busy inhaling. Wimsey raised his head, and with it his voice. I quickly shoved the liver into his mouth. I knew from several previous unfortunate incidents that although spectators were usually charmed by Wimsey's vocal offerings, judges and handlers seldom were. We hadn't even entered the ring yet and already we were getting dirty looks. I hustled Wimsey into the ring before he could decide that he wished to play another round of the bribe my nose off the carpet game or to place a loud order for more liver.

"Wimsey, trot," I trilled and shoved another piece of liver into his mouth. Given that he had paced his way around the breed ring, no one was more surprised than I-- except perhaps Maria--when he actually did. It was a pity that I had to take back on him so soon to forestall what was almost certainly going to be an in-depth exploration of the adjacent Rhodesian ridgeback's anus.

Unlike the trotting, Wimsey dismissed the stacking in the usual way, his quotient of cooperation having apparently been exhausted. And although clearly disappointed by the lack of an elkhound, he had decided that the ridgeback would make an acceptable substitute. Out of the corner of my eye, I could see its handler edging away from us.

I was just debating how to supply Wimsey with some ridgeback-free entertainment when I remembered his session with the animal communicator. I looked around furtively and began to jump up and down in what I hoped was a discrete manner. This was clearly magical thinking. I was standing in a show ring dressed entirely in green (including a shiny new green headband I had found in a children's store) and trying to control a large dog with a small string.

My jumping seemed to attract everyone's attention except Wimsey's. His was focused entirely on extorting a free-flowing river of meaty snacks in exchange for not baying or challenging the ridgeback to a wrestling match. But free flowing rivers of meaty snacks lead to free-flowing rivers of drool and by the time we reached the head of the line Wimsey had enough saliva in his flews to marinate me and anyone else unlucky enough to be standing nearby. I applied the drool rag with exceptional diligence and used it to vigorously wipe not only the outside of his mouth but the inside of it as well. It was only when I was absolutely certain he was dry that I moved him into position in front of the judge. It was a distance of perhaps ten feet. The judge took Wimsey's face in his hands and immediately recoiled. Then he extended a slimy hand and glared at me.

"He drooled on me!" he exclaimed, stating the obvious in an exceedingly peeved way. "Do you have a rag?"

I did have a rag, but I also had a dilemma. I could already see some sticky stalactites forming around Wimsey's mouth and if history was anything to go by, they had a high probability of becoming imminently airborne. I had only a fraction of a second to decide whether to hand over the rag or to wipe Wimsey's face. The judge was wearing a nice sport coat. I wiped. It was a tossup as to whether the judge was more annoyed that I had presented him with a slobbery rag or a slobbery hound. I noticed that the remainder of Wimsey's examination took place rather more rapidly and at a greater distance than usual.

"Down and back" he said while keeping an eye on Wimsey who danced around, impatient for the resumption of his interrupted mealtime.

"Wimsey, trot!" I said and showed him a piece of liver. Wimsey trotted. It was a large ring and never before had I gotten so much trot out of him. And if you discounted the fact that his nose was pointed towards the piece of liver in my hand, he might even have looked better than he had at Westminster. He came to a brief and polite halt in front of the judge and then rammed me forcefully in the abdomen in the spot where my treat pouch would normally have been. The judge decided he had seen enough of both of us and as we returned to our spot and Wimsey once again resumed his fluid trot. The only time he had looked this good was when he had trotted for the orthopedic vet when he was supposed to be lame.

The class was large so I thought it possible that we might make the first cut. We didn't. Whether this was because Wimsey had failed to impress the judge or had impressed him too much was an open question.

"What happened?" Maria asked when she met us outside of the ring. "Wimsey looked great."

"Wimsey slimed the judge," I shouted as Wimsey bayed and tried to separate my right arm from its shoulder.

"But just wait until next time." I predicted. "Next time is going to be great!"

CHAPTER 26--IT'S A BLOODHOUND WORLD

There is generally an upside to everything if you look hard enough and in my case it was that Wimsey's antics both in and out of the show ring meant that I always had plenty of entertaining material for his blog. But in addition to being fun to write, Wimsey's blog also came with some unexpected benefits. Companies began sending us products for Wimsey to review and while he was happy to munch his way through the assorted bags of snacks that Chewy.com sent we were happy to try out the assorted canine accoutrements that also arrived. These were usually the kinds of things you would expect, like collars, bowls and leashes but sometimes it was obvious that marketing departments hadn't actually read the blog. For instance, neither Maria nor I were eager to install electric fences in our apartments nor did we think that Wimsey would enjoy wearing earrings. And we didn't really think that Cesar

Millan wanted Wimsey's opinion about the new dog training video he sent us, especially since he showed up from time to time as Wimsey's nemesis in the blog's fantasy sequences where he had an unfortunate tendency to explode or to come to some other equally unpleasant end. Nevertheless, we posted a clip of Wimsey watching the video while seated on the Tribute Couch being hand fed slices of pizza. It was the only photoshoot for which he actively cooperated.

The blog also had other, less tangible benefits. Wimsey was now recognized by more people, including those from out of town, like the excited woman from Georgia who ran down a hill in Central Park screaming his name. He also received emails from readers who were planning to visit New York and wanted to see him along with the city's other celebrated tourist attractions. One of these emails came from a couple from Finland who were both bloodhound owners and blog fans. It was a lot of fun to take them around Central Park while discussing the fascinating foibles of the breed including a digestive system so odiferous that it prompted one of Wimsey's other Scandinavian readers to name her bloodhound Wrinklefart. Wimsey enjoyed the moose chews the Finnish couple gave him and we enjoyed seeing the article they wrote about him for a Finnish bloodhound magazine.

But what surprised us most about the blog was not its far-flung readership or the unorthodox range of products that Wimsey was asked to endorse, but how many of its readers were convinced that it was entirely a work of fiction. And whereas this was undoubtedly true when it came to the blog's fantasy sequences in which Wimsey proudly shared stories about how his many illustrious ancestors were responsible for everything from the Norman Conquest to winning the Revolutionary War or when he engaged in a number of improbable, Walter Mitty-like professions such as running an airline, a hotel or a restaurant or being a psychotherapist, a language teacher, or a judge or when he was the subject of CNN Special Reports by Wolf Blitzer and Anderson Cooper or when he gave interviews as his French alter-ego, Monsieur le Hound, people were frequently skeptical when I told them the rest of the stories were actually true. It probably didn't help matters any that while I was telling them this Wimsey would sit placidly at my feet radiating obedience and cooperation. People took one look and thought that I was either crazy, lying or had stumbled upon some really cool kind of dog that I didn't want anyone else to have. We also received emails like the one below:

Wimsey, I met you in the park in NY. I am a lab breeder and I saw you and fell in love. Well, I wrote you and you advised me not to buy a bloodhound and check into the breed. Well, I did. And yes, I did buy a bloodhound named Madam Molly Margaret from a lady who shows and trains bloodhounds. Well, after 1 month, we changed her name to Monster Molly. Molly has chewed up everything in sight. Even my new end tables and the slats around the swimming pool. She brings everything in the house. Even mud balls from the garden. One thing is for sure, the kids have learned to pick their stuff up! I don't know about you but she loved going swimming in the pool this summer. Molly is now going to school every day for obedience, it is not going so well. It is like the movie Xmas Vacation and someone yells "squirrel!" She has a small attention span. But we are coming along. Just a little bit longer. But she is the funniest dog you will see. She is always looking to see

what kind of trouble to get into. Just wondering... does this
run in your family?

> *Best,*
> *Sharon*

I should have carried a copy of it with me along with a few other social media posts, like the one about the bloodhound who ate through a living room wall to create a shortcut to the kitchen or the one who chewed a bloodhound-sized hole in his owner's mattress or another who stole a wallet and ate only the twenties. People who own other breeds compete to see whose dog is the best, bloodhound owners compete to see whose is the worst.

But few stories impressed us as much as that of Gus the Alaska Bloodhound. Gus was owned by Edie, an elementary school teacher from Fairbanks whose family included two daughters and two coonhounds. As an experienced wrangler of large hounds and small children she didn't foresee any problems in adding a bloodhound to her pack.

Fast forward a couple of years. We received an email from Edie telling us how much solace Wimsey's blog had given her. She had been at her wit's end and had googled "bad bloodhound." One of the first things to pop up was *Diary of a Manhattan Bloodhound* and as she read through it she realized that she didn't have a bad bloodhound. She had a regular one.

That being said, Gus was in a league of his own. Bloodhounds tend to be specialists and if Wimsey specialized in bending humans to his will, Gus specialized in the destruction of their property. The toll he took on Edie's was epic, especially since she told us he was never left alone.

The damage included:
Large chunks of dish towel
Pillow stuffing
Queen sized comforter
Rope
Barbie dolls
Plastic milk jugs
Assorted plastic lids
A bucket

Logs for the fire

Assorted toys

Pincher bugs

Beef rib bones

Chicken bones

A salmon

Sticks of butter with wrapper

Moose poop

Vacuum cleaner attachments

Remote controls

Artwork hung on walls

Tanned beaver fur

Gum

Twenty socks

Rocks

Tennis balls

Shoes

Soap

Feminine hygiene products

Flowers

Dirt from potted plants

The potted plants

Bras

Panties

Gentle Leader

Assorted leashes

The carpet

Coffee grounds

Candles and ornament from a birthday cake

A cactus

And that's not counting both the arm of the couch and a blanket he managed to eat while still locked in his crate. As a bloodhound he was brilliant, as a dog he was awful.

Several months later we were very excited when Edie emailed us to say that she was going to be chaperoning a school trip to New York. We were really looking forward to meeting her and were horribly disappointed when we realized too late that we didn't have any way to contact her once she arrived.

On the afternoon of her arrival, Wimsey and I were on our way to Central Park as usual when we ran into a couple we had met when Wimsey tried to inhale one of their feisty dachshunds.

"How's this week's blog post coming? We really love reading it," the woman said as she commenced massaging Wimsey's ears.

"Oh, I have a funny story about one of its readers," I replied. And then I told her about the woman from Alaska who thought she had a bad bloodhound until she read the blog.

"Wait! Is her name Edie?" the woman exclaimed.

"Yes! How on earth did you know?" I was stunned.

"She's a friend of mine. In fact she and the school group are staying at the church where I work. Do you want her number?"

When it comes to bloodhounds six degrees of separation are apparently five too many.

That evening Wimsey took Edie and her two daughters on an extended tour of Central Park where he demonstrated the proper way to tree squirrels, climb up on high rocks so we couldn't make him come down without injuring him and deposit poop where we couldn't get it. While Wimsey entertained her girls, Edie told us about how she used portions of Wimsey's blog to teach reading. We thought it might also be fun if Wimsey taught American history so after Edie returned to Alaska we sent her some lessons. The lessons were very popular. Although there might be people in Alaska who think that Washington crossed the Delaware with a very large bloodhound perched in the prow of his boat.

But if the bloodhound world was small, nowhere was it smaller than in the dog show world where Wimsey's blog also made the rounds. Through it we met Kim and Michael, dedicated bloodhound show people from California. We were all taking a walk in Central Park together one afternoon when I began to complain about Wimsey's behavior in the show ring.

"Oh no," Kim protested. "Much worse things can happen." Then she told us about Clancy.

"Clancy and I were waiting for the judge's examination and he got bored. Suddenly, he swung around behind me, got up on his hind legs, grabbed my waist with his front legs and began humping me. That would have been bad enough," she continued, "but he also lifted my skirt when he did it. People were turning away so they wouldn't have to look."

But that wasn't the end of it.

"Afterwards my son was showing him in Junior Showmanship. Clancy got away from him, jumped three rings and landed right smack in the middle of the Yorkshire terriers. Handlers were screaming, picking up their dogs and running. As I was chasing him around the ring I heard someone say, 'It's THAT dog again.' I was mortified."

The story made me feel oddly better somehow. But I made a mental note never to let Wimsey stand behind me in the ring.

CHAPTER 27--LOVE AND THE SINGLE SHOW DOG

A few weeks before Wimsey's next show, we received an email from Julie, a student at the International Center of Photography who had read Wimsey's blog and wanted to include him in her senior project on the lives of Manhattan dogs. I warned her that Wimsey was perhaps not the best of subjects given his low opinion of cameras but she was still game so we made arrangements to meet for one of Wimsey's weekend walks in Central Park. The good news was that since Wimsey's weekend walks took an entire day to complete she would at least have plenty of time to watch him not cooperate. And as usual, Wimsey didn't disappoint--he bayed, dragged, and flung drool with abandon; he attempted to play with small dogs who were terrified of large ones; he ran away when he saw the camera; he demanded whichever snack I didn't happen to have; and if we even so much as hinted that we were ready to leave the park, he threw himself on the ground and waved his legs in the air.

Julie was charmed.

So charmed in fact that we invited her to watch Wimsey give us a bath and to come with us to his next show in East Orange, New Jersey.

The problems began almost immediately. We had just gotten ourselves, Julie and Wimsey settled into Ray's SUV when I turned the key in the ignition and nothing happened. The battery was as dead as one of Wimsey's stuffies. Given my proficiency at pumping gas I had little wish to see if I could avoid electrocuting myself with jumper cables so I ran around the corner to the local Hertz office instead. It seemed like a much better option right up until the moment that I signed the credit card slip for $200. But as painful as that was, it was nothing compared to the pain of Wimsey baying directly into my ear as soon as we pulled into the parking lot in East Orange. He was carrying on even before his paws hit the pavement and as soon as I opened the car door he shot out of the vehicle like he had been ejected from a canon. And unlike in Westchester, this time he galloped straight to the building's entrance dragging me behind him.

"I think Wimsey's in a mood," Maria declared when she caught up.

It was a frightening thought. Even in the best of times Wimsey was not easy an easy dog but Wimsey "in a mood" was the DEFCON 1 of difficulty: if I attempted to walk him in one direction, he would drag me in the opposite one; if I relented and went that way then he no longer wished to go that way but wanted to go in another one. Or even worse, he would refuse to move at all until I guessed in which direction he wanted to go. And all while he bayed non-stop--he wanted a snack…no, not that snack, a different snack…he wanted to play with that dog over there…why wasn't that dog over there interested in playing with him…he wanted to meet that human over there… why wasn't that human over there giving him their water bottle, pizza, sandwich, ice cream, etc.

Even before we entered the building, I had a feeling that this was not going to be our finest hour.

Once inside the reason for Wimsey's "mood" became immediately apparent. Karen, our new friend from Westminster, was standing by the bloodhound ring and where Karen was Phoebe was also. Wimsey had probably picked up her scent even before we had pulled into the parking lot.

"Hopefully there will be a lot of other males between him and Phoebe," I said to Maria.

There weren't. Wimsey and Phoebe were the only two bloodhounds to show up. I wanted to disappear. Although the winner was a foregone conclusion, I was not looking forward to the experience.

The nightmare began as soon as I tried to get Wimsey into the ring. Male dogs go before females. Wimsey did not approve of this system since it meant removing his nose from where it had taken up residence in Phoebe's backside. I tugged, but neither Wimsey nor his nose moved. I finally gave up and dragged him into the ring while he did another one of his *Exorcist* impressions. But only temporarily. As soon as Phoebe took up her spot behind him his body followed his head so that everything was now pointing in the same direction--backwards. Before I could even begin to fight with his feet I had to fight with the rest of him just to try to get him facing the right way. But Wimsey resisted all my efforts--shockingly even those accompanied by liver--and stood like a statue, touching noses with the Phoebe and gazing adoringly into her droopy eyes. It would have been a charming scene had we not been in a show ring.

I abandoned what was clearly going to be a losing battle and pushed, him over to the judge. But the judge's charms were no match for Phoebe's. He tried to run back to her.

I apologized to the judge. Apologizing was the only part of show handling in which I was becoming proficient, the only variation being the specific nature of the infraction that needed apologizing for.

"I'm sorry, I said, "he's kind of in love with that dog."

The judge regarded me icily.

"Down and back," he said with a notable lack of sympathy as Wimsey once again tried to run back to his lady.

By dint of some serious shoving, I managed to get Wimsey three steps down and three steps back. It was perhaps the shortest down and back in history. Since the judge was clearly losing patience with the whole Dog v. Handler display I muscled Wimsey over to the rail for his trot back to his spot. It was wishful thinking. He tried to cut across the ring to get back to Phoebe and when I stopped him he took off at a gallop that terminated with his nose jammed forcefully into Phoebe's rear end.

It was a good thing she liked him otherwise he would have been a bloodhound in more ways than one.

But Phoebe just ignored all the snorting going on in her lady bits and walked calmly over to the judge for her examination. It was cursory to say the least, the choice being obvious. But Wimsey didn't care how short it was. He was annoyed by Phoebe's absence and began to protest loudly. And when this failed to produce the result he wanted he dragged me over and joined Phoebe next to the judge.

The judge handed Phoebe's handler the Best of Breed ribbon and avoided looking at me and especially at Wimsey when he handed me the one for Best of Opposite Sex. Wimsey wasn't the Best of Opposite Sex, he was the Best of Opposite Everything, including being a show dog. He exited the ring with his nose once again attached to Phoebe's hind end. The only pictures our photography student had managed to get were of Wimsey putting his nose where it didn't belong. I apologized to her too.

The ride home was uneventful. Or it was until I dropped everyone off and went to return the car.

"What's the matter?" Maria asked, when she saw my face "I mean apart from the obvious."

I showed her the final bill.

"What!" she cried. "$100 for extra cleaning! Wimsey was only in the car for forty-five minutes."

I guess that battery was trying to tell me something.

I should have listened.

CHAPTER 28--ARE YOU BEING SERVED?

I learned very quickly that Wimsey was a dog who didn't just want you to serve him, he expected you to. Whenever he wanted something he would stare at you in the way that an absolute monarch stares at an unsatisfactory minion and make you feel like you were a particularly disappointing specimen of humanity if you failed to get him what he wanted quickly enough. It might be a toy, or a bone or a snack that he had shoved under the couch because he liked watching you retrieve it for him. Or perhaps he wanted his ears scratched. Or his water bowl refilled. Or his water had too much drool in it. Or he wanted more food. Or he wanted your food. It was a look that was as impossible to ignore as it was to resist. And whereas bloodhounds are notorious for stealing food, Wimsey never did. He never had to.

Apart from the lack of larceny, Wimsey's approach to food was unusual in other ways as well. For instance, its value often depended less on what the food actually was than on how it was served and by whom. Apples were a perfect example. One afternoon Wimsey had been taking a nap on the futon when I sat down on the couch to eat one. And although Wimsey may have been asleep, his nose never was. It sprang into action and was quickly followed by the rest of him. I bit off a piece of the apple, 100% certain that he would reject it. He didn't. And not only did he take it and not spit it back at me but he hovered around the couch like a large fruit bat until I gave him more.

I didn't get to eat much of my apple—in fact Wimsey seemed to resent me actually eating any of it--but I was extremely pleased, nonetheless. Given how fickle and finicky Wimsey's food preferences were, finding a new food item with which to bribe him was like winning the lottery. I couldn't wait to tell Maria all about this exciting new development in the Wimsey snack universe. But when she arrived after work she listened with a frown of skepticism on her face.

"Wimsey doesn't like apples, she declared. "I eat them all the time and he has absolutely no interest in them."

'Well he likes them now," I replied. "I'll show you." Maria watched in silence as Wimsey dripped drool on my feet and thwacked me with his paw if I failed to feed him fast enough. Finally, she spoke.

"It's not the apple Wimsey likes. He likes that you are taking it out of your mouth and giving it to him. I eat mine sliced on a plate and he won't touch them." I tried it. She was right.

But Wimsey was particular about other aspects of food service as well. One afternoon, instead of an apple, I sat down with a bowl of popcorn. Wimsey, as usual, arrived to investigate. I offered him a kernel. He sniffed the kernel. He ate the kernel. He liked the kernel. He ate all of the kernels. The next day, in the interests of actually getting to eat my popcorn, I prepared a second bowl, identical to the first. Wimsey squeaked like one of his stuffies as he pranced over to the couch. I offered him a kernel. He ignored it. He just stood there staring at me. I couldn't figure out what he wanted. Then it hit me. The kernel I had offered him had come from the second bowl. He didn't want popcorn from that bowl. He wanted popcorn from mine.

All of this also helped explain an earlier mystery. Maria called me one day shortly after I had started regularly doing Wimsey's afternoons walks.

"I'm so sorry," she said. "I baked a tray of brioche before work and I left them to cool on the kitchen table and forgot to put them away. Wimsey probably made a mess eating them and his stomach might not be too great either." But when I arrived, the brioche were sitting unmolested on the kitchen table exactly as Maria had left them. And why shouldn't they be? There was nobody there to serve them to him.

Wimsey's service requirements also extended to liquid refreshment. The three of us were in the park one Sunday when Wimsey dragged me over to a water fountain for the fifth time in as many minutes to fill the new portable water bowl I had recently bought for that purpose. Maria turned to me.

"You do realize Wimsey isn't actually thirsty. He just likes it when you serve him water." And whereas this was undoubtedly true, I still wasn't the one who squatted down like Maria did and held the bowl up to his mouth because bending was bad for his back.

And it wasn't just us that Wimsey had this effect on. We had a lot of company. Like the waiter who chased us down the street shouting and waving a breadstick. We naturally assumed that Wimsey had peed on something he wasn't supposed to or had done something else equally egregious to one of the restaurant's patrons seated at the outdoor tables--Wimsey treated outdoor tables like they were open air buffets and would make his way down them sampling the food people offered him like a guest at an All You Can Eat. I turned to the waiter to apologize for whatever it was Wimsey had done but before I could open my mouth he presented the breadstick to Wimsey.

"I'm sorry," he said (to Wimsey), "it's the only thing I could reach on short notice. Next time I'll have something better for you." Wimsey graciously accepted both the apology and the breadstick. And when Wimsey bayed at a woman all the way down 72nd Street because she was eating an ice cream, she, too apologized to him.

"I'm so sorry," she said her voice oozing regret. "I would give it to you but it's chocolate and could make you sick. How about this nice cookie instead?" Even among supposedly callous New Yorkers it was astonishing how many people were willing to disgorge sandwiches, pizza, pretzels, doughnuts or anything else they happened to be eating all for the unalloyed pleasure of watching Wimsey enjoy them. One gentleman even insisted on buying him a roast beef sandwich.

And although ice cream was one of Wimsey's favorite foods it too had special service requirements. We happened to be passing an Italian restaurant on our way to the park when Wimsey stopped to bay at a dog across the street. The manager came out to see what was going on.

"Your dog is absolutely adorable!" she exclaimed as Wimsey turned his attention to snuffling the kitchen odors on his new admirer. "Would he like a cup of gelato?"

"I'm sure he'd love a cup of gelato," Maria replied. "Wimsey is exceptionally fond of gelato."

Fond was perhaps understating the case a bit. Grom Gelato had recently opened a store on Broadway and Wimsey dragged us there in high decibel cry at every opportunity. Patience not being his strong suit, the fact that he had to wait for me to go inside and stand in line to buy him a cup made him insane. It was touching when people thought it was me he wanted. The staff, however, knew better. As soon as the heard him, if they weren't busy or it was before they had opened or after they had closed for the night they would come out and offer him a cup. Free of charge. They even knew he liked vanilla. Curbside service was also available when I had to shout my order instead of going in because Maria wasn't there to hold his leash. And like so many other of his activities, Wimsey's gelato eating always drew a crowd although apparently the restaurant manager had never been among them. She emerged from the restaurant and placed the cup on the ground. Wimsey stared at the cup. Then he stared at her. His face had the "What the hell is this?" expression that appeared whenever he was confronted by an unfamiliar object, circumstance or phenomenon that he suspected he was not going to like.

Finally, he turned and stared at me. The manager was as confused as Wimsey.

"Doesn't he like gelato?" she asked.

"Oh no, he loves gelato," Maria replied. "But he wants a spoon."

And it wasn't only the means by which a snack was offered or the route by which it was fed that mattered, but also by whom. If I offered Wimsey a snack when he and I were out alone, he took it. If Maria was with us, he wouldn't. He would stare at me until I gave it to her to give to him. If I handed his leash to Maria, then he would take snacks from me. But not from her. It was one person's job to hold his leash and the other person's job to feed him snacks. It was Wimsey's way of maximizing the number of people serving him.

A similar rule applied when Wimsey made the rounds of neighborhood pet shops or other venues--such as my local liquor store--that had dog snacks on the counter for canine customers. He was happy accept these offerings from staff members but if one of them chanced to be intimidated by his size and asked me to give it to him, he would refuse. I had to scour the store until I found a more courageous employee.

One of Wimsey's main snack squeezes, and consequently a spot that he dragged me to with alarming regularity was The Boat Basin Café, (not to be confused with The Boathouse, the restaurant in Central Park that was the purveyor of Wimsey's favorite tuna fish sandwiches). The Boat Basin Café was a dog-friendly outdoor eatery adjacent to the Hudson River Marina and its primary attraction--apart from the beer that Wimsey insisted I drink so he could play with the plastic cup afterwards--was the large box of Milkbones that sat next to the cashier. Wimsey's relentless pursuit of this grocery store snack far exceeded any enthusiasm he showed for the healthy, expensive organic ones I spent hours researching online. But sometimes the cashier was either busy or too worried that Wimsey's Milkbone fervor might extend to her fingers so the task of Milkbone dispensing fell to the Boat Basin's manager of whom Wimsey was exceptionally fond.

One day, there was a crisis in Milkbone Land; the manager reached into the box and it was empty. It was difficult to say who was more upset, Wimsey or the manager. The manager kept apologizing. Wimsey kept staring. Then he had an idea.

"Wait here a second," he said and trotted off through the swinging doors that led to the kitchen. When he emerged he was carrying a plate piled high with bacon.

"I just couldn't bear to disappoint him," he explained. That was the problem. No one could.

But sometimes serving Wimsey came with unintended consequences. Such was the case of what came to be known as The Great Popsicle Stick Mystery. It had its origins in a chance encounter in Central Park between Wimsey and my friend Nancy and her toddler Alicia. Wimsey adored Nancy and whenever they met he put on elaborate displays of baying, scampering, wagging, standing on his head and presenting his belly. I'm sure it was only a coincidence that Nancy was always in possession of a stroller full of toddler snacks and had a generous nature. Alicia, too, was generous so when she had concluded her interactions with the popsicle she was eating she offered the rest to Wimsey. Nothing seemed untoward.

The little girl held out the popsicle and Wimsey, as usual, did his dainty frog imitation and licked the stick.

It was only when it was time to leave that I noticed that Alicia's hands were empty. I looked around for the popsicle stick intending to dispose of it but it was nowhere to be found. I was puzzled. Wimsey was an experienced eater of park popsicles but his interest had never extended to the stick itself. I inspected his flews anyway—perhaps he intended to carry the stick home to add to his extensive collection of miscellaneous objects that he kept in our apartments. But his flews were empty. I even looked down his throat but nothing seemed amiss there either.

I had Wimsey's vet on speed dial.

Sirena, the receptionist, answered the phone.

"Hi Elizabeth, how's Wimsey?" What she really meant was what's the matter with him this time.

"He may have eaten a popsicle stick," I explained and shuddered to think about its effect on Wimsey's internal organs as well as the bill to repair them.

"Let me check with Dr. F," she replied. She returned several minutes later, an interval that Wimsey used productively to renew his unsuccessful campaign to induce Nancy's terrified little Yorkie to play with him by baying maniacally at it.

"Dr. F says to give him olive oil and pumpkin to help the stick pass and to observe him closely for signs of distress."

Maria was also on speed dial.

She answered the phone with,

"What's he done?"

"He probably ate a popsicle stick."

"Impossible. Wimsey never eats popsicle sticks," she replied.

"Well, he decided to try one. We have to feed him olive oil and pumpkin and monitor him closely."

She sighed. "He'll like that, especially the monitoring part."

As Maria had predicted, Wimsey not only appreciated our diligent surveillance of his rectal regions but also reveled in the fact that we now found his every bowel movement to be a riveting event. And not only did we watch him intently during the evacuation itself, but upon its completion we methodically inspected the results with gloved fingers while he stood by and beamed at us, clearly pleased that his excrement was finally being accorded the respect it deserved rather than being thoughtlessly tossed aside in a bin.

We were not surprised that Day One proved unproductive since the length of Wimsey's colon rivaled that of the Lincoln Tunnel. We were more optimistic on Day Two. But Day Two also failed to yield results as did Days Three and Four. On this day, Maria insisted that I show her the exact spot where the popsicle stick had disappeared, convinced that I had somehow overlooked it. Finding nothing she had another idea.

"Is it possible he digested it?" she asked.

I thought for a minute. "Not unless Wimsey is harboring a colony of termites in his gut or is part beaver," I replied. I regarded him speculatively while he investigated some sandwich remains.

There were really only three possibilities: 1) in spite of extensive searching I had failed to find the stick either on the ground or in Wimsey 2) in spite of even more extensive searching Maria and I had both failed to find the stick in Wimsey's poop 3) Wimsey had somehow acquired the ability to digest wood. All three were impossible but then again, objects--even those involving Wimsey--did not simply disappear.

On Day Six I had just entered Maria's apartment to collect Wimsey for his afternoon walk when I saw it. There, in the middle of the floor was a popsicle stick. But not just any popsicle stick. It was a popsicle stick that looked as pristine as the day it had rolled off the factory floor. There was not a speck of poop or vomit on it. Nor could I find any poop or vomit anywhere else in the apartment either. I inspected Wimsey's mouth for signs of blood or trauma and finding none, I proceeded to the other end. His anal region proved similarly devoid of any sign that it had been in contact with a foreign object. I phoned Maria.

"HOW is that possible!?" she exclaimed. "SIX DAYS! What was it doing in there!? And how did it come out all by itself and clean?"

It was, like so many things involving Wimsey, a mystery. What was not a mystery was that it was time for Wimsey's duck heart. He was staring at me.

CHAPTER 29--WIMSEY LIKES IT LOUD

File under gluttons for punishment: we decided to enter Wimsey in the three day Eastern Regional Bloodhound Specialty in Harrisburg, Pennsylvania. This prestigious show would give me the opportunity to take Wimsey into the ring (or vice versa) for three days in a row, which I hoped would improve the skills of at least one of us.

A week before we were due to leave, however, the drama of Wimsey's career inside the show ring was again mirrored by our transportation difficulties outside of it. Preparations and Excel spreadsheets were well underway when we learned that that Ray's car was once again out of commission which meant that we were once again at the mercy of New York's piratical rental car companies. And in some delusional burst due to either an excess of gin, optimism or frugality I had somehow convinced myself that

Wimsey and three-day's worth of his stuff could all fit into a compact car. Fortunately the point was moot. When we went to pick it up they were all out of compacts.

"But we do have this one for you," the clerk said with a smile on her face and handed me a set of keys in a way that indicated she thought I would be pleased. I wasn't. I was horrified. They were the keys to a Jeep Commander and the largest thing I had ever driven was Ray's diminutive RAV4. In terms of size the RAV4 could be described as an SUV in the opposite way that Wimsey could be described as a dog. Not only was I uneasy about driving something that big but my legs were too short to get into it, my arms too short to attach the GPS to the windshield and I couldn't reach the pedals unless I moved the seat up as far as it would go. I drove it to Maria's like a recent graduate from the Erwin Rommel School of Automotive Arts. And then when I got there I had the privilege of entertaining a street full of people who gathered to watch me try to parallel park. I've had better starts to my day.

The only one happy was Wimsey. As soon as he saw Maria remove his harness from the closet he knew exactly what was up. Or more precisely exactly what was down. He gave a whole new meaning to the phrase race to the bottom and when he burst through the front door he was baying like a banshee. I flung open the car door and leapt aside. Quickly. Past experience had taught me that if you were in Wimsey's way you didn't stay in Wimsey's way for long. But when Wimsey tried to get into the car it seems that I wasn't the only one challenged by the unaccustomed height of the vehicle. He stood up on his hind legs, planted his front feet on the seat like he usually did, but when he reached for purchase with one leg, he found only empty air. On impulse I sprang forward and wrapped my arms around his midsection to help him.

Maria rolled her eyes.

"Wimsey is perfectly capable of figuring out how to get into the car by himself," she said. Given that he and I were about the same height she was undoubtedly correct. But Wimsey disagreed. My momentary lapse in judgement meant that thereafter Wimsey refused to enter a vehicle of any size without me providing this new and wholly unnecessary service. He would stand with his front feet on the seat and stare expectantly at me over his shoulder. I had forgotten the cardinal rule that if you did anything Wimsey liked once, you did it forever. Like how toweling him off after a heavy downpour meant having to towel him off after even the slightest drizzle. The car was just another example of how while I was always trying to train Wimsey, Wimsey was always trying to train me. And I had yet to come out on the winning end of the equation.

The drive to Pennsylvania was mostly uneventful, (if you didn't count me almost filling up the tank with diesel) and by the time we arrived the hotel was already in the throes of a serious bloodhound infestation. There were bloodhounds everywhere. They lazed about the lobby like lounge lizards at cocktail hour. Since it wasn't necessary to hide Wimsey in the car he came with us to check in. While paperwork and credit cards flew back and forth he stood up on his rear legs and followed the intricacies of the process with such an intelligent and attentive expression that at any moment I expected him to start ordering room service

We drove around to the back to our adjoining rooms and as soon as we let Wimsey loose in them he set about figuring out which one of them was mine so he could occupy it and which of the two beds I wanted so he could claim it. Since I slept badly with him and Maria slept badly without him, it was a total win-win for him.

We decided to leave the connecting door open anyway on the off chance that Wimsey would actually choose to sleep where we wanted him to. But much like Melville's Bartleby the Scrivener, Wimsey preferred not to. I had no sooner climbed into the bed that I didn't want than I heard the sounds of creaking, digging and snoring coming from the bed that I did. Somewhere in the wee hours, however, Wimsey decided that he had exhausted all possible rearrangements of his own bedclothes and it was time to move on to mine. He climbed up on the bed, shoved me to the side and began to mangle the blankets. When he was satisfied with the result, he lay down with his head on my pillow and snored in my ear. Sleep (mine) was over for the night.

The next day did not start out well and not just because of what I looked like after a night spent being snored at by Wimsey. The show was being held at the Pennsylvania Farm Center and when we arrived we discovered that it actually was a farm center--like the kind with barns and animals.

"I was about to say, 'I don't think we're in Kansas anymore' but I think we really are," I observed to Maria.

Whether we were in Kansas or Pennsylvania Wimsey was thrilled about the abundance of domestic wildlife and as soon as we let him out of the car he made loud and muscular attempts to access the barns. Maria grabbed his collar, I choked up on his leash and together, inch by noisy inch we dragged him into the large building that housed the show. Unfortunately what we found inside offered little improvement over what we had found outside. The place was teeming with bloodhounds and people who smelled like bloodhounds. Wimsey began to bellow even louder.

We located an unoccupied spot and while Maria set up Wimsey's crate Wimsey got busy trying to shove his nose into the backsides of anything with four legs or two. Thwarting these attempts only made him louder and I was just started to rummage in my treat pouch for something to shut him up when the Star Spangled Banner began to blare forth from the loudspeakers. Everyone stopped what they were doing to face the large flag hanging from the rafters. Everyone, that is, except for the people near us. They stopped what they were doing and faced me. And hissed. By the time we got to Wimsey's robust rendition of the rocket's red glare, I wished I were elsewhere.

Even after the anthem was finished Wimsey continued to bay, unabated and unappeased, no doubt encouraged by all the attention his patriotic sing along had received. I was therefore very much relieved when we got to our ring and I saw that our class was a small one. It meant that today's visit to the Farm Center would at least be short. Wimsey even stopped baying long enough to devote himself to trying to extract liver from all the places I had carefully hidden it. He obviously thought that show rings were a new kind of chain of snack meat restaurants. He took a brief and grudging break from liver hunting to pace and trop his way around the ring and was awarded zero ribbons. But as soon as we exited the ring Wimsey's voice once again soared above the fray. The building's acoustics were excellent and the only time we saw anyone smile at us was when we packed up to leave.

We returned to the hotel and Wimsey immediately climbed up on top of the table in my room so he could look out the window and keep tabs on all the activity in the large field below. It was abuzz with people walking dogs and socializing around the picnic tables that had been set up. At dinner time Maria and I raided the Fairway bags, slipped a Halti on Wimsey and went down to join them. Chris from Trenton was there and she introduced us to her husband Steve and their bloodhound Brady. But the highlight of the evening was not the meal or seeing Chris again but that at bedtime Maria lured Wimsey into her room and shut the connecting door. I could hear his nails scratching on it as I fell asleep.

Day Two at the Farm Center (carefully timed to occur after the playing of the National Anthem) was no more peaceful than Day One. Wimsey appeared determined to break his record for non-stop baying. In the interests of escaping all the glares and stares his efforts were attracting I decided to take him for a walk. He charged energetically out the door and dragged me from barn to barn like an inspector from the Department of Agriculture. Every moo, oink and baa seemed to require his immediate attention.

It was only when we returned to the show that the full impact of Wimsey's cow canoodling became apparent. He had mud, muck and hay stuck to various bits of him and he trailed the distinct and pungent aroma of freshly turned manure. People started sniffing the air around us as we passed.

"Oh my God!" Maria exclaimed when she saw (and smelled) him. "Where has he been? Never mind, I don't want to know." She got out the Crown Royal and towels.

It was clear that my second attempt to show Wimsey was going to be a far different experience from my first. We were at the back of the pack of a very large number of bloodhounds. And even worse, almost as soon as we entered the ring, Wimsey showed signs of being disenchanted with my entertainment value. No doubt disappointed by my failure to provide a pig or a sheep for his amusement, he began to scout the landscape for something that was a better option than me. He quickly found it. Steve and Brady were standing just outside of our ring and as soon as he saw them he tried to make an airborne exit out of the ring. Then when I blocked him he made a run for it under the rail instead. I pulled him out by his dewlap. He was just in the process of trying to squeeze himself through the two middle rails when Steve noticed the commotion and took Brady out of range. Wimsey protested this move vigorously.

Neither food nor wrestling could placate him. I even tried jumping up and down. Wimsey continued to bay. It was only when we moved up for the judge's examination that he finally fell silent. This was usually Wimsey's favorite part of the proceedings. He liked having his skin and body parts played with and especially liked having testicles admired. But now as soon as I tried to prod him into position, he wheeled around, planted himself squarely in front of the judge and began to bay. I was mortified.

"Wimsey be quiet!" I ordered, although I knew this would probably make him bay even louder.

"No," the judge said, "let him do it. He's a bloodhound, he's supposed to." As this was distinctly a minority opinion, I wondered where he stood on the matter of having his pants poked or drool flung on his face, both of which appeared to be imminent.

"Down and back please," said the judge before Wimsey could put it to the test. The judge looked him over carefully and when his examination was finished Wimsey took off like a rodeo clown to the spot where the scent of Brady was strongest.

We didn't win.

Maria and I decided to console ourselves by doing some shopping at the show's large and distant retail area. At least here Wimsey would get to annoy a whole new group of people. And he loved shopping. He and I had spent many happy hours touring the aisles of the pet shops he dragged me to so he could sniff all the merchandise, especially that relating to cats. He was a canine connoisseur of kitty litter.

While Wimsey indulged his nose, Maria and I hunted for bloodhound-themed merchandise. There wasn't any.

"They're not a popular breed," one merchant explained to us.

"I can't image why not," I said as I pulled Wimsey's nose out from under some lady's skirt.

On the final day of the show neither Wimsey's attitude nor my handling skills showed any signs of improvement. As we exited the ring, Heather Helmer, a well-known professional bloodhound handler, approached us. She gave me her card.

CHAPTER 30---CLOSE ENCOUNTERS OF THE NEW YORK KIND

Wimsey may not have won anything in the show ring but he did win the battle to stay as far away from it as possible. We might have been more successful if he had demanded ribbons from the judge the same way he demanded gelato from Grom. But he didn't, and at the end of the day I was reluctantly forced to conclude that trying to make Wimsey do anything that Wimsey did not wish to do was good for neither my mental health nor my liver. There is a very good reason why you never see bloodhounds on any of those dog training TV shows.

Liberated from my futile attempts to train him for the show ring, Wimsey was once again free to enjoy himself doing what he did best-- following scent and entertaining his fellow New Yorkers, usually at my expense. Walking Wimsey in a city like New York was always something of an adventure because you never knew who you might run into. In my case, literally.

One Sunday, for instance, Maria, Wimsey and I were just about to pass the Delacorte Theater in Central Park when we noticed a large family group pointing at us and heading rapidly in our direction. There was nothing in itself unusual about this or about them except perhaps for the unusually meticulous grooming of the middle-aged man leading the charge. From the crease in his khaki pants to his impeccably pressed blue shirt to the full head of hair with not a strand out of place, he looked like he had just stepped out of the pages of a magazine. I immediately shortened Wimsey's leash. Well-dressed people never seemed to heed my warnings about what Wimsey would do to their wardrobe until he did it. But in this case the man seemed so genuinely delighted and surprised to find a dog like Wimsey in a place like New York that I relaxed my grip. I think it was somewhere between our deep dive into Wimsey's life, loves and character and Wimsey's deep dive into a baby's diaper, that I had the vague sensation that I had seen this man somewhere before. Could he have been one of my clients from Wall Street? He did have that portfolio manager look about him. Or maybe he was a famous actor or soap opera star? He definitely had that look about him too. In fact, he was neither. He was Mitt Romney. Maria told me later. And I had been on the verge of asking him what he had been in recently.

I did, however, recognize Al Franken the day he stopped to pet Wimsey. Maria told me it was not the first time these two had met. Wimsey and Al Franken's Labrador had shared a puppy nanny and he had admired Wimsey back then too. It was a pity the same could not be said for the puppy nanny who finally refused to take care of Wimsey owing to his persistently mistaking her bed for a toilet and to his complete lack of interest about what she had to say on this or any other matter. She told Maria that Wimsey was a very disobedient dog. But he was a consistent one.

Al Franken aside, New York is a celebrity-laden town and Wimsey and I had undoubtedly run into our fair share of them but I had about as much luck recognizing them as I had with Mitt Romney. Even when Wimsey took a break from hunting people eating pizza to hunt film and TV crews, unless Maria was with us I couldn't tell the sound guy from the star. And although Wimsey usually found them, sometimes it was the other way around. Maria and I had just sat down on a stone bench next to the Central Park lake because Wimsey wanted to admire the ducks when a man detached himself from a phalanx of cameras around Bethesda Fountain and came running towards us. Even I could tell he was an actor. He was stunning.

"I love bloodhounds!!!!" he cried--probably because he had never had one--and plunged his hands deep into Wimsey's dewlap. Wimsey turned his attention from contemplating duck à l'orange to assessing the entertainment possibilities of his admirer's pale green suit. The man must have seen the look on my face.

"It's OK," he assured me. "We're done shooting for the day." Even so, I was glad I wasn't going to be the one who had to explain to the wardrobe department.

"Why is it," I asked Maria after he had left, "that people wearing light colored clothing always seem to think it's a good idea to pet Wimsey?"

"Well at least his suit was green," she replied. "Diane Sawyer's was white. I told her we were in a hurry. And I ran."

"Anyway, do you know who that guy was?"

"Of course I know who he was!" she exclaimed and gave me one of those incredulous looks that she usually reserved for when I rewarded Wimsey for doing something really obnoxious because I thought it was funny, or when I cut up his pizza into two-inch pieces because he liked it that way or when I told her that we had taken a five hour walk because Wimsey didn't want to go home. "That was Matt Bomer, the star of *White Collar*."

Wimsey and I actually ran into *White Collar* quite a bit after that, although given the prowess of Wimsey's nose and the fact that the rest of the cast and crew also liked dogs, was probably not a coincidence.

"But I'm impressed that he knew Wimsey was a bloodhound," Maria added. "When we ran into Robert Redford he asked me what kind of dog Wimsey was."

"Did you tell him a bad one? I bet Paul Newman would have known. On both counts."

But to be fair, Robert Redford was actually in the majority. We often got asked what kind of dog Wimsey was. Very few people seemed to have ever met a bloodhound in person or realized just how big they really were—but then again, neither did Wimsey. Or maybe it was just that people couldn't believe that anyone would be crazy enough to have one in New York City.

Wimsey was also frequently the victim of mistaken identity. The combination of his size, his wrinkles and his color seemed to confuse people, although some of the choices defied explanation:

Great Dane (big), Mastiff (bigger), Bull Mastiff (biggish), Irish Wolfhound (super big), St. Bernard (big, but shaggy?), Newfoundland (also big but shaggy?), Dogue de Bordeaux (wrinkles and red), Shar Pei (more wrinkles), Irish Setter (really red, but long hair?), Cane Corso (cropped ears? and fierce?), Rottweiler (black and tan-ish, but fierce?), Fila de Brasileiro (bloodhound origins, but even fiercer?), Basset Hound (right family, wrong dog),

Coonhound (ditto), Boykin (a spaniel-y breed?), Black Hound (is this even a breed?), but the prize for the most imaginative fantasy breed goes to the man who asked us if Wimsey was a Pirate Hound. Wrong yet strangely right.

And on the subject of fantasy breeds, Maria and I had one of our own. It started when Maria told me that she and Wimsey had been in the park when he suddenly started baying and dragged her out the exit and across the street to the American Museum of Natural History. There was a large crowd peering through the fence on the side lawn and Wimsey shoved his way to the front of it and thrust his snout through the bars. The only thing Maria could see was a woman standing in the grass.

"What's everyone looking at?" she asked a man who was staring intently. The man pointed to something that looked like a large curved rock rising a bit above the grass.

"It's the Museum's pet tortoise," he explained. "He's out for a walk."

Maria thought that walk was perhaps stretching it a bit. But in spite of the fact that the tortoise appeared to be distinctly non-ambulatory, everyone was pretty excited by it, especially Wimsey. Maria said that his nose was twitching so violently it looked like it would split. And although she was able to drag him away using a Halti. Wimsey returned so frequently thereafter to check if the tortoise had reappeared that we dubbed him The Black and Tan Terrapin Hunter.

But in addition to purebred dogs we also got asked if Wimsey was a mix of different breeds, including Doberman Pinscher and German Shepheard. And sometimes we weren't even asked. We were told. People would even argue with me after I told them that Wimsey was an AKC registered champion who had been shown at Westminster three times. One guy absolutely insisted that I was wrong and that Wimsey was a mix of Doberman Pinscher and St. Bernard and another swore that Wimsey looked exactly like his brother's Bull Mastiff. Had I told them that Wimsey was a Black and Tan Terrapin Hunter they probably would have told me that their best friend had a Black and Tan Terrapin Hunter and that Wimsey didn't look like him.

But perhaps they wouldn't have been so quick to argue with me if they had ever seen Wimsey's nose in action. Like when he caught a whiff of a newly hatched mound of horse manure somewhere in the park and took off after it baying like he was in hot pursuit of a juicy boar. Or when I returned home from a business trip and the first thing I heard was the sound of Wimsey baying at my window from across the street. He had probably picked up my scent as soon as my taxi crossed the bridge to Manhattan.

"He knows you're in there," Maria would text, "and he's not going anywhere until you come down."

We got a real kick out of it when people would ask us in all seriousness, "Did you know that bloodhounds have a very powerful sense of smell?"

But not all encounters were as entertaining as the man walking his terrier in the park one evening who offered us a drink and then opened his jacket to reveal a full-sized bottle of Côte de Rhone, a corkscrew and several wine glasses. New Yorkers are famous for many things and never being shy about expressing an unsolicited opinion is definitely one of them. It's something you learn very quickly if you have a kid or a dog, particularly if it's a dog like Wimsey. Much to our surprise (and occasional amusement given the irony), Maria and I were often accused of mistreating him. The reasons ranged from forcing him to live in an apartment, to not letting him off his leash or even to addressing him as "Hound" when we were exasperated with him.

Lady: "Is his name Hound?"

Me: "No."

Lady: "Then don't address him that way. It's very disrespectful."

Unfortunately she stalked off in a huff before I got a chance to tell her that we usually addressed Wimsey as "Sir" in deference to his belief that he is a reincarnated king of France.

But there were other matters that also drew a stern rebuke from the general public, like refusing Wimsey's demand for yet another Belgian waffle from his favorite waffle truck (he took his with extra whipped cream) or refusing to hand over my frozen yogurt after he had finished his. And it always seemed to be somewhere around Hour Four of one of Wimsey's extended Central Park dragathons that someone would scream at me that I was a terrible person because a dog like Wimsey didn't belong in New York City and needed a backyard. Wimsey had a backyard--it had 843 acres and contained people who thought I was a terrible person.

And then there was the ever contentious matter of Wimsey's testicles. Those who didn't admire them were enraged by them. People yelled at me about them so often that even before anyone said anything I said,

"HisnameisWimseyhe'sashowdogsoheneedshistesticles." I never imagined that I would spend so much of my life discussing testicles.

Wimsey, as you might expect, had a few grievances of his own to add to the list. Like when Maria occasionally refused to sleep on the sofa when he wanted the bed (or if she did, then if she refused to swap places in the middle of the night when he wanted the sofa), or if she attempted to stifle his baying at 5:30 am when he wanted to announce to the neighborhood that he was now out for his morning walk or when either of us didn't immediately replace a member of the size-ordered stuffed hedgehog collection that he kept in both our apartments when he had shredded one. It was a good thing Wimsey couldn't talk.

But we were on the receiving end of at least one "suggestion" that was much easier to implement than banishing Wimsey to some suburban enclave. The Upper West Side has a very large dog population and it was hard not to notice that the dogs were often much better dressed than the people holding the leash. They wore raincoats in wet weather, sweaters in chilly weather and winter coats of down or fleece in cold weather. And it wasn't just small dogs either. The fashion parade included dogs of all sizes, breeds and mixes. You might see anything from a formidable-looking lady Rottweiler trundling down the street in a blue pastel jacket with matching booties to a fluffy Siberian Husky braced against the cold in a fleece hoodie.

It was an understatement to say that the sight of a naked bloodhound in the neighborhood was not well-received. People were incensed and we were coat shamed on a regular basis. I did try to explain that Wimsey didn't actually need a coat because large, furry mammals retain heat due to their favorable surface to volume ratios, but this explanation was about as popular as the one about why Wimsey needed his testicles. I bought Wimsey a coat.

Wimsey, as may be supposed, was not wholly in favor of this new development in his life. The first time I tried to get him into it he pressed himself against the wall and glared at me irately. It was only after I produced some turkey that he realized that the coat had possibilities he had initially failed to consider. I'm sure he also enjoyed the fact that if a bloodhound in the middle of Manhattan is difficult to ignore, then one wearing a gaudy, chartreuse fleece is even more so. Wimsey cut such a striking figure in it that it was like he was walking the red carpet every time he walked out the door.

We were even stopped by a British morning TV show doing a segment on how New Yorkers (or Wimsey) cope with the cold. It was no doubt due to the dazzling nature of Wimsey's wardrobe that they were willing to overlook the disheveled state of mine and the fact that my nose very possibly dripped even more secretions than

Wimsey's flews. I only hope no one was trying to eat breakfast when it aired.

Wimsey's fleece was fine when it was just cold but I noticed that it got soggy when the weather was also wet. I added a second coat to Wimsey's wardrobe that was supposed to be good for both. It was made of a stretchy, red fabric that was insulated and water-resistant and clung to Wimsey like a Speedo.

"The Ruff Wear website says the coat is designed to provide maximum range of motion to the more active and athletic canine," I told Maria as Wimsey modeled my new purchase during a snowy walk.

"Do they have one that provides minimum range of motion to the more active and athletic canine?" Maria asked as Wimsey curvetted, cavorted and caprioled in the snow like a Lipizzaner who had ingested too many cups of coffee.

I saw her point. Although Wimsey's feet had the ability to adhere to snow and ice with a Spider Man-like tenacity, ours did not. On the other hand this only seemed to add to the enjoyment of those who gathered to watch the Wimsey Ice Capades.

Wimsey loved everything about winter. His love of fresh powder rivaled that of any Olympic skier and it sent him into a joyous frenzy of plunging in and rolling around for extended periods. Eventually even the Red Speedo got wet so I had to buy him a second one to wear while it dried. It was black with silver piping and made him look like Tron. It was very much admired by everyone except Wimsey.

We were much less successful in the matter of booties to protect Wimsey's feet from the salt on the sidewalk. Even with both of us sitting on him he possessed an almost supernatural ability to both tear off booties and eat turkey at the same time. I'm sure it's because he preferred the more personal approach of us carrying warm water and rags and washing his feet and spraying them with Pam whenever he lifted a salty paw.

But it wasn't just winter wear that got us in hot water in the neighborhood. We got raincoat shamed as well. The result was that I bought Wimsey so many brightly colored raincoats that he looked like a refugee from a Crayola box. His red one with a hood was especially popular. It happened to match one of mine, something I only realized when people asked me to stand next to him for a picture. The only other time people wanted me in their pictures was when Wimsey sat next to me on a bench and loomed over my head in way that made me look like a resident of Munchkin land.

I actually had a terrific time buying Wimsey clothes. It was fun making him look ridiculous for a change. Revenge was sweet and none was sweeter (except perhaps for his Christmas hat collection) than his cooling coat. The irony was that it was the only coat that Wimsey actually needed and whose purchase was not driven by public opinion but by the fact that although Wimsey thrived in the cold, he reacted to heat like a vampire at noon. He darted from one shady patch to another with his tongue hanging out in a way that made me feel like Cruella de Vil every time I took him out.

The coat had a silvery blue reflective material on the outside and multiple layers of absorbent polymer underneath. When it was soaked in cold water the layers absorbed the water and then slowly released it to cool the dog. But in spite of the fact that the coat was very effective and that he panted much less and could stay outside much longer, Wimsey hated it. As soon as he saw me soaking it I would find the front part of him—the only part that fit—under the bed. Then once I got him into it and outside he would take off at a gallop, convinced that if only he ran fast enough he could outrun it. For such a crafty dog he could be surprisingly obtuse. But Wimsey wasn't the only one who hated the coat. If people yelled at us in the winter for having a naked dog, then they yelled at us in summer for having one that was dressed.

We also discovered that if Wimsey's winter coats made him look silly, then the cooling coat made him look important and official. Maria overheard one gentleman confidently explain to his companions that Wimsey was on dangerous police business because he was wearing a bullet proof vest. Too bad that the only thing Wimsey needed protection from was us, especially since he had recently decided that chasing "squirrels of the night" (aka rats) make for some good summer fun.

But my favorite case of cooling coat mistaken identity occurred one steamy afternoon when Wimsey and I were waiting for the light to change on Broadway.

"Miss, do you need help crossing the street?" I heard a voice behind me say.

At first I was annoyed. I always hated it when people assumed that because I was small I couldn't handle Wimsey. Like the crowd of doubters in the park one day who were of the opinion that if I could walk Wimsey then he must not be all that strong. I offered to let them test that idea by giving them partial hold of Wimsey's leash. The men lined up to pit their strength against his like he was a carnival game. Suffice it to say that none of them would have walked away with a stuffed animal. Wimsey's pedicab friends also used to debate my ability to handle Wimsey until the day I wore a tank top and they saw my biceps. Maria always said she didn't need a gym, she had Wimsey. And cancelling her membership was not an option.

But in this case, I suddenly realized that the man's offer of help had nothing to do with my size. It had to do with Wimsey's cooling coat. He thought Wimsey was a seeing eye dog.

Just then Wimsey bayed and tried to drag me into traffic.

I guess he realized his mistake.

CHAPTER 31---ROAD TRIP!

Maria's face fell when she read the email.

"Jan and Trudy cancelled their trip," she announced. Jan, whose husband you may recall was responsible for accidenting Wimsey into existence, and her friend Trudy, who owned Wimsey's sister, Dixie, had been planning to come East for a visit. We had been looking forward to meeting them and especially to re-introducing them to Wimsey whom they had not seen since he was small enough to actually fit into someone's lap.

"Well, we could always rent a car and take Wimsey to visit them instead," I suggested. It seemed like a good idea at the time, but then again, most things usually did when I had a gin and tonic in my hand. Maria, who did not have a gin and tonic in her hand but a substantial portion of

Wimsey in her lap, shot me a skeptical look. But then she had an idea.

"You know, if we did that then we could stop off on our way to Jan's place in Michigan and visit my mother in Buffalo. She's dying to meet Wimsey." I was sure Wimsey was dying to meet her too. She was Hungarian and every month she sent him a tin of home-baked Hungarian honey cookies the merest touch of which sent him flying out of the bedroom to make sure Maria didn't eat any.

Things fell into place quickly after that. We arranged to spend a few days in Buffalo before making the long drive to Grand Rapids since there weren't any hotels in the tiny town of Sand Lake where Jan lived. We would then break the journey again in Buffalo on the way back. When Trudy found out we were coming she emailed to say that she would drive in from Illinois with Dixie and make it a true Wimsey family reunion. Wimsey was a big fan of all the trip planning. Whenever Maria sat down at the computer, he would stretch out with his rear legs on the loveseat and his front ones on the desk so that when Maria looked at her computer screen the only thing she could see was him.

After the dates had been set and the hotels had been booked, we still needed to rent a car. A really, really big one. When we made a list of the (disturbingly large) number of things Wimsey would need for eight days on the road it looked like it would fill a truck. And since large, sheddy drooly hounds were about as popular with rental car companies as they were with hotels, I decided to take a few creative liberties when I paid them a visit.

"I need an SUV that is large enough for three 'passengers' *(two humans and a humongous space-hogging hound)* and a lot of 'camping equipment' *(or several jumbo bags of kibble, an elevated feeding station, stacks of leashes, multiple collars, harnesses, gentle leaders and other, mostly ineffectual means of hound control, a collection of size-ordered stuffed hedgehogs, a collection of rawhide bones ((nubs included)), a collection of ((bone-shaped)) animal bones, a collection of miscellaneous non-hedgehog stuffies ((including Doggy who Wimsey carried around and squeaked in our faces when he wasn't feeling well or needed to go out)), a mountain of quilts, comforters and other soft nest building materials, cartons of bribing snacks, a Fairway bag of cleaning materials, several bottles of Febreze and Crown Royal, a hand-held vacuum and as many sheets and towels as it took to transform a hotel room into something that looked like it had been decorated by Christo).* I also have an extremely large 'painting' *(or a folded dog crate big enough to house a mountain lion)* and the car needs to have rear garment hooks so I can hang 'clothing'" (or *a zip line for the harness that one of the passengers needs to wear because he's under the impression he has a driver's license).*

No one was even remotely curious about what kind of camping trip involved a painting and crisply pressed clothing. But then again, this was New York, a city where I once saw a man walking down Fifth Avenue painted green and wearing a toga, and people barely glanced.

After visiting all the rental car companies, I finally found what I thought I was the perfect SUV at Hertz. But just as I was about to book it, I happened to look inside and noticed that it had rear bucket seats.

"Oh, I forgot to mention that I need bench seating in the back. One of my passengers is….um…very large and he won't fit into those seats." It was the only true thing I had said. But to be fair the real reason we needed bench seating was because Wimsey liked to stretch out across the back seat when he napped.

"Well couldn't the large passenger sit in the front, since that seat is bigger?" the man asked.

"No, I don't think that would be a good idea," I replied, although I was fairly certain that the large passenger would think that it was an excellent idea. Fortunately, the rep was able to find a substitute and I signed on the dotted line before he could ask any more questions about my peculiar camping trip that now included a passenger so large that he didn't fit into the bucket seats of an SUV.

On the day of departure, however, our streak of last-minute transportation difficulties remained unbroken. I handed the clerk our rental information and she frowned.

"We no longer have this vehicle," she said. "But let me have a look in the back and see what we've got."

"It can't have rear bucket seats," I called out, as she disappeared into the recesses of the garage before I could tell her about the painting, the clothing hooks and the camping equipment.

We paced about nervously but when the clerk finally returned it appeared that the automotive gods had smiled on us once again. The new vehicle not only met all of the criteria for our unorthodox camping trip but it was even bigger than the one I had originally booked.

We were just congratulating ourselves on our good luck when I pulled up in front of Maria's building and tried to get out. I couldn't. The door was locked and there didn't seem to be a handle or anything else designed to facilitate our egress. Instead, there were a large number of buttons with mysterious icons like the one I had once pressed that engaged a trailer hook instead of the headlights. We began frantically punching buttons that did everything except open the door. It was like playing Escape the Room but without the clues. Maria even tried consulting the owner's manual which contained a wealth of information about everything related to the car except how to get out of it. I guess they assumed that if you could drive you could open a door.

"You're going to have to call the garage and ask," Maria concluded.

"No! I refuse to be a stereotype."

Probably because I was.

"Well, what's this one do?" she asked, and reached over and pressed a small, cryptic-looking square that we had somehow overlooked. The doors clicked open.

We hadn't been this excited since we had escaped from the bathroom.

The next hour or so we spent sweating like stevedores as we hauled Wimsey's stuff down five steep flights of stairs and piled it all into the car. When we were done I checked the rear-view mirror and the only thing I could see was Wimsey's luggage. And while this made a change from seeing Wimsey it was just about as useful.

"It's no use." I said after our multiple loadings and reloadings resulted in only a tiny square of visibility, "I'll just have to use the side mirrors. At least Wimsey can't block those." This wasn't strictly speaking true. He actually could. He just couldn't block both of them at the same time. I'm sure it annoyed him greatly.

We moved on to the seats, every square inch of which we had to swaddle in multiple layers of sheets. Maria had once tried using a canvas seat protector for pets but Wimsey had managed to shed hair under it anyway. For a dog who could put kibble in your underpants it wasn't much of a challenge. The seat protector joined the Wimsey graveyard of other effective devices, like no-pull harnesses and anti-shedding tools.

Meanwhile, the delay caused by both getting into and out of the car plus all the loadings and unloadings had thrown Wimsey into a state of frenzied anticipation. When Maria finally put on his harness he flew down the stairs like a Stuka and leapt into the car so excited that he forgot that he needed my help to get into it. We were on our way!

Or almost. We still had to get out of Manhattan which, if you didn't count dealing with Wimsey, was always the most challenging part of any trip.

Things I Have Learned Driving in Manhattan:

1.   Taxis have the right of way. Always. No matter what. Even if they cut you off. Don't mess with them.

2.   Worry about what's in front of you, not what's behind you. It's the job of the guy behind you to worry about that.

3.   Lane lines are only suggestions.

4.   If you leave a space in front of you, a car will fill it.

5.   If you use your directional signal to let other drivers know what you want to do they won't let you do it.

6.   If you're trying to pull into traffic and a car hesitates for a split second, he's letting you in.

7.   If a car has out of town plates it will do stupid things (there is a reason why I am ecstatic when our rental cars have plates from states we are not driving in).

8.   Having an old car is better than having a new or expensive one. Their owners have more to lose.

9.   Big cars outrank small cars.

10.   Trucks outrank everyone (except maybe taxis). They are the apex predators and rule the road. Accept it. They will mow you down.

11.   A showdown between a truck and a taxi is like Godzilla vs. King Kong. Enjoy the battle but stay out of the way.

12.   Drive down side streets at a crawl— anything or anyone that is lurking between parked cars where you can't see them will dart out in front of you. It's a rule.

13.   Pedestrians are like Wimsey—they don't believe red lights apply to them.

Having successfully made it out of Manhattan, we were happily cruising along the open road when a few hours later I noticed the gas gauge was getting low. It had been several months since our last excursion to a gas station so while I reviewed the gas pumping process, Maria busied herself trying to figure out how to open the tank. It was going about as well as trying to get out of the car (although considering that it had once taken us thirty minutes to figure out how to open a package of Wimsey's string cheese, it wasn't much of a surprise).

While I pursued my studies and various parts of the car that were not the gas tank flew open, out of the corner of my eye I could see a man get out of the car behind us. He had a very unpleasant look on his face. He began to yell when Wimsey, detecting the pleasing aroma of an annoyed human, poked his head out of the window to get a better whiff. The man stopped in mid-shout. A big grin spread across his face.

"That's a great-looking dog!" he exclaimed. "Here, let me give you a hand."

"Wow," I observed to Maria as I got back behind the wheel, "Wimsey got a guy to pump gas for us! For once he was actually useful."

"Yes, but if he knew that he'd have hidden under the seat."

In spite of the momentary glitch at the gas station, we were making very good time. Or we were until we hit the New York-Pennsylvania border. I had noticed a nasty-looking thunderstorm just ahead when suddenly it was like we were trying to drive through Niagara Falls. The windshield went completely opaque and there was zero visibility. I put on the hazard lights, slowed to a crawl and hoped that we didn't hit anything or end up in a ditch. I was also worried about Wimsey's reaction. But Wimsey, the dog who bolted in terror at the sight of a man doing tai chi in the park, had decided that thunder, lightning, pounding rain and humans who were re-evaluating their relationship with the Almighty, were insufficient reasons to abandon a highly satisfying nap. He was snoring.

The storm was large and violent and seemed to go on forever. The lane lines put in only the briefest of cameo appearances. But at last, ever so gradually the rain lessened. How we managed to stay on the road I had no idea but when I could finally see out the windshield again, I decided to pull into a rest area and take a much-needed break. As the car rolled to a stop, Wimsey joined us in the front seat again. He wasn't wearing a harness.

"I think he needs a new harness," Maria observed unnecessarily as she viewed what was left of the current one in the back seat.

I did my best not to send free-range Wimsey flying through the windshield and several hours later, much to everyone's relief except his, we pulled into the parking lot of The Lord Amherst Motor Hotel. I went in, alone as usual, to check in. The place was deserted so I rang the bell on the front desk. Eventually, a woman appeared, and she was not happy about me interrupting whatever it was she had been doing.

"I'd like to check in two people and a dog in two rooms," I said and gave her our information. She punched aggressively at her computer.

"This doesn't say anything about a dog," she snapped. "Now I have to rearrange everything! We only put dogs in certain rooms." She pounded angrily on her keyboard before she finally thrust a couple of key cards in my direction.

Our rooms were at back of the property and while Maria unloaded the car and draped the room, I waited discretely in the car with Wimsey.

When she had finished, I pointed to a grassy area adjacent to the building.

"Let's see if we can get Wimsey to pee in that field," I suggested.

Pottying Wimsey on the road was an endurance sport. He was convinced that the purpose of any rest stop was to catalog everything and everyone who had been there before him and no matter how much we pleaded and cajoled, he seldom undertook any activity that did not involve his nose.

We watched anxiously as Wimsey inspected the field. It seemed like success was finally within our grasp when suddenly, out of nowhere, disaster struck! A small, brown jack rabbit broke cover from behind a bush. Wimsey froze. He had never seen a jack rabbit before, and he stared at this one like it had just stepped out of the *Star Wars* cantina. His nostrils flared violently and he crept forward cautiously, one tentative step at a time. Given my extensive experience in the matter of Wimsey v. Squirrel I knew exactly what was going to happen next. I tightened my grip on the leash, dug my heels firmly into the earth and braced my arm for potential dislocation. But Wimsey didn't lunge. In fact, he didn't even move. He stood as still as a statute and gawked at the exotic little creature. The rabbit, who noticeably agreed with me as to the likely course of events, took a few prudent hops out of range. And then all hell broke loose. Squirrels did not hop. Rats did not hop. Mice, racoons and cats did not hop. People not handling him in the show ring did not hop. Sensing imminent death, Wimsey screamed and bolted backwards with a force so powerful that my upper body looked like a corkscrew.

"He's afraid of rabbits!!!! I shrieked, when I could breathe again through the pain. What kind of dog is afraid of rabbits!!!"

Maria grabbed the leash and sighed.

"This is Wimsey we are talking about," she replied. It was her stock answer to everything from why products meant to reduce flatulence gave him more of it, to why dark meat chicken gave him diarrhea but the rich Norwegian cream cake she baked for his birthday didn't.

We moved away from the field but Wimsey remained skittish and scanned the horizon suspiciously for more threats of a rabbity kind. He begrudged us one small pee (on a very distant tree) and made it clear that his confidence in our ability to protect him from dangerous wildlife was minimal in the extreme

"I don't think he's going to do anything until he forgets about that rabbit," Maria observed. "We might as well go upstairs. I don't know what you did to that desk clerk, but just wait until you see the dog room."

I was glad she warned me. The room was dark, dingy and worn and judging by its odor it had some serious issues with its plumbing. It smelled even stronger than Wimsey and that was saying something given that it had been a full 48 hours since his last bath. Wimsey poked about happily, delighted that we had finally found him a room that smelled nice.

My room, in contrast, was lovely, if for no other reason than it didn't smell like either sewage or Wimsey. After we had unpacked, we dowsed Wimsey with a quantity of Crown Royal and got back in the car for the

short drive to Maria's mother's condominium complex.
The complex was a large property dotted with two-story
brick buildings. It was so quiet, green and immaculate that
it looked more like a movie set than an actual place to live.
Wimsey immediately tried to remedy this by peeing on an
ornamental bush he wasn't supposed to.

Maria's mother was waiting for us in front of her
door at the top of the stairs. She was a lively woman who
positively bristled with a warm and welcoming energy.
Most of it was directed at Wimsey. One energetic nose
wanding of her dress told Wimsey all he needed to know.
He had found the source of his beloved Hungarian honey
cookies. Wimsey velcro'd himself to Maria's mother with a
devotion heretofore unknown in his behavioral repertoire.
Her every move merited his undivided attention and he
supervised her activities in the kitchen like a Parisian chef
de cuisine. The only thing missing was a toque and an
apron. When Mrs. S opened the refrigerator, he thrust his
head in to inspect what was being removed; when she
chopped, stirred or poured, he gazed at her with the soulful
expression he usually reserved for the lady hounds. She
was so enchanted that she kept up a spirited, if one-way,
conversation with him to which Wimsey listened with a

look of such rapt attention that it could not help but flatter its recipient.

While Mrs. S cooked and chatted with Wimsey, Maria and I sat down in the living room to have a drink. Presently, Mrs. S, (with Wimsey attached), emerged from the kitchen. She was carrying a plate of Hungarian hors d'oeuvres called pogácsa and she deposited them on the coffee table. Wimsey placed his chin on the table and gazed at the cheesy delights with the rapturous look of a medieval monk venerating a relic. Mrs. S lovingly fed him one, beaming at his obvious appreciation. Periodically she poked her head out of the kitchen to admonish us to feed him.

Dinner was a delicious chicken paprikash (Maria had a vegetarian version), a substantial amount of which had found its way into Wimsey's food bowl. When we were finished eating and Wimsey had finished extracting additional supplies, Maria's mother went to the refrigerator and took out a plate of elegant-looking rolled Hungarian dessert crêpes. Maria followed her into the kitchen and removed one.

"What are you doing with that?!" her mother asked rather sharply. She ruled her kitchen with the same democratic spirit as an Eastern potentate.

"I'm going to give it to Wimsey," Maria replied.

"He can't have that!" she responded even more sharply. Maria looked at her puzzled.

"Why not?" she asked.

"It's cold!" her mother declared and gave Maria a look of such ferocious horror that it was like she had proposed serving dirt for dinner.

"Give me that!" she said and snatched the crêpe away. "I have to heat it up for him."

Wimsey enjoyed the crêpe.

The next day, Maria and I offered to run over to Wegman's to pick up some items needed for that evening's dinner. Maria's mother looked at us with consternation.

"But what will you do with Wimsey?" she asked.

"Wimsey can stay here with you," Maria replied.

"But won't he be upset when you leave?"

"Wimsey will be fine," Maria replied drily. When
we left he barely looked up from his food bowl. There were
pogácsa in it.

If Hungarian cuisine was Wimsey's treat,
Wegman's was ours. We were enthralled by its broad,
clean, well-stocked aisles, its helpful staff and its complete
absence of shoppers who wielded shopping carts like
snowplows. We wandered its spaciousness aisle by aisle
like refugees from the former Soviet Union.

We were gone a ridiculous amount of time but
when we returned we found that we weren't the only ones
who were beaming.

"Wimsey is wonderful!" Mrs. S proclaimed even
before we had a chance to cross the threshold. Since this
was generally a minority opinion among anyone who had

spent much time in his company--the bloodhound trifecta of hair, stink and drool not being especially popular--we were naturally curious as the specific nature of this wonderfulness.

"He wasn't at all bothered that you left!" Mrs. S declared. Maria looked at me.

"Duh," she muttered cynically.

"He followed me everywhere and when I sat on the couch (heavily draped), he lay down next to me and put his head in my lap. He's an angel! I love him!" Wimsey might think he could outrun cooling coats and that rabbits were rattle snakes, but he definitely knew on which side his pogácsa were buttered.

On our last night, Mrs. S thought that instead of Hungarian food I would enjoy a taste of Buffalo's claim to culinary fame She placed a heaping mound of chicken wings in front of me (I fear my appetite compared very unfavorably in her view with Wimsey's) and another in front of herself. But she wasn't eating hers. She was methodically deboning them and hand feeding the meat to Wimsey.

Wimsey was not happy when we left.

CHAPTER 32---ROAD TRIP PART TWO

The next morning we reloaded the car, reloaded Wimsey (now smartly turned out in the new harness that the clerk in PetSmart assured us was foolproof) and hit the road for the ten-hour drive to Grand Rapids. Somewhere in western Pennsylvania Wimsey climbed into Maria's lap. I glanced over my shoulder. His new harness was lying intact but useless atop a pile of plush bedding. I was impressed. Not only had he managed to extricate himself, but he had done so with a stealth and dexterity that had failed to attract our attention. Houdini couldn't have done it better.

We made a pit stop to insert Wimsey back into the foolproof harness and began the long drive through Ohio. It was like being in an automotive remake of *Ground Hog Day*. No matter how far we drove there was always the same cornfield, the same red barn and the same straight road mile after mind numbing mile. If I incur a karmic debt in this life, I'm certain my punishment will be to drive through Ohio in the next. And if I do really bad things, I'll being doing it with Wimsey. He had escaped from his harness again and alternated between using my left shoulder as a chin rest and investigating the contents of my left ear.

I thought we'd never make it out of Ohio but when we did it was a relief to find that Michigan had hills and roads that curved and was green. We also discovered that its rest areas were pet friendly so when we stopped for lunch Wimsey was welcome to eat our sandwiches at a picnic table instead of in the car. The rest stop even had a specially marked doggy hiking trail that was devoid of rabbits and had vegetation that Wimsey deemed worthy of several important leg lifts. Maria was less of a fan. She marched down the middle of the path like she was wearing a straitjacket.

"Look over there! That's poison ivy!" she would cry.

"I don't think that's poison ivy."

"Well how do you know?"

"Because it's a bush."

"Well, it could be a bush of poison ivy."

There is a reason we live in New York City.

Several hours later we pulled into the parking lot of the Baymont Inn in Grand Rapids and I realized I might have made a colossal mistake. When I booked the hotel, I had failed to notice that it had multiple stories and a layout that wasn't of the motor inn variety. This meant that we couldn't just pull the car up to our rooms but would have to get to them through a lobby. With Wimsey.

As far as I was concerned, the fewer people who saw Wimsey the better, and while it was true that we had never actually been kicked out of a hotel, we had come close. I could still hear the screams of the guests at a Sheraton in Silver Spring and the staff's tactful suggestion that we use the elevator by ourselves. This wasn't much of a problem since no one would get into it with us anyway.

Certainly not the lady who shrieked and hid around the corner every time she saw us.

I was understandably not in a relaxed state of mind when I went to check in.

"Well?" Maria asked when I returned.

"So far, so good," I replied. "We don't have adjoining rooms, but they were expecting a dog and they didn't ask any inconvenient questions about exactly what kind." I eyed Wimsey who was baying and jumping around in the back seat.

Maria handed me Wimsey's shortest leash and we headed to the front door.

"Here goes," I said, and pushed it open.

The lobby was crowded. And every head in it swiveled in our direction. We tried to look nonchalant as we walked to the elevators, squeezing Wimsey between us like we were going to a show ring. I could feel the eyes following our progress. We found an empty elevator, shoved Wimsey unceremoniously into it and hit the close button. Hard. When the door opened on our floor, I poked my head out to make sure the corridor was empty. Wimsey poked his head out to make sure it wasn't a show ring.

But when Maria opened the door to Wimsey's room we were in for a shock.

"Oh my God!" I exclaimed. "It's huge. And look at that big couch." Compared to the other places we had stayed with Wimsey this was a Four Seasons.

Maria draped the room with such excessive care that when she was done it looked like she was going to paint it. Then the phone rang. We looked at each other. When you've just paraded through a hotel lobby with a dog the size of a miniature horse phone calls were probably not a good thing.

"Hello?" I said tentatively.

"Hi this is John from the front desk." I could feel the knot in my stomach tighten. "I'm just calling to make sure everything is okay."

"Yes, thank you," I replied, trying to keep the relief out of my voice.

"Great! Let us know if you need anything."

I was pretty sure he didn't mean a Valium.

I turned to reassure Maria on the couch but the only thing I could see was her legs. Wimsey had joined her.

The next morning Jan and Trudy met us in front of the hotel and while we got acquainted with them Wimsey got acquainted with his sister. This mostly consisted of him baying and shoving his nose incestuously up her backside.

"I thought that before we drive to Sand Lake, we could stop off at a dog beach on Lake Michigan. How does that sound?" Jan asked.

"That sounds great!" I replied. "I've always wanted to see Wimsey swim. In Central Park swimming isn't allowed so I only let him wade in up to his shoulders. That way if we get caught, I can say that he wasn't actually swimming."

Both women had come in Trudy's minivan which had its middle seats ripped out so Dixie could stretch out. There was also a water bucket hanging on a hook into which Wimsey stuck his head. It seems that although Dixie was generous about allowing Wimsey free access to her backside, her water bucket was a different story She growled at him and snapped. Wimsey promptly fled to the safety of our laps and we made the trip to the beach pinned to the back seat.

The beach, however, more than made up for the discomfort of getting there. It was a large and deserted expanse of sand with gentle waves lapping at its shore. I put Wimsey on his thirty-foot leash and walked him over to the water to await what was sure to be exciting aquatic developments. And there were exciting developments, just not aquatic ones. Wimsey froze and stared at the gentle waves the same way he had stared at the jack rabbit. Then he bolted backwards with his tail tucked between his legs.

"What happened?" Maria asked. "Why isn't Wimsey swimming?"

"He's afraid of the water." I replied. 'It's moving."

But if Wimsey was afraid of the water, he unfortunately had no such reluctance when it came to the sand. To the contrary, he seemed determined to embed the maximum amount of it in his coat When he wasn't rolling around in the dunes like a beach ball he was racing back and forth and kicking up fine layers of it into his fur. Periodically he took a break to pay loud and unwanted attentions to his sister. And no sooner had we dragged him off her than he would wheel around, stare suspiciously at the waves and then take off again with me gasping for air behind him.

A good time was had by nobody except Wimsey.

"Maybe he'll swim in Sand Lake," I said to Maria as we tried to de-sand him. "Given its name it presumably has one. And hopefully one with less terrifying waters."

"And less sand," Maria replied as she wiped away the clump that Wimsey had just flung in her face.

Sand Lake did indeed have a lake. It was a quiet lakeside village of only a few hundred people and when we had finished eating lunch at an outdoor café and shouting conversation at each other over the sound of Wimsey baying for my sandwich (which he got) and Dixie (which he didn't), I turned to Jan.

"Can we see if Wimsey will swim in Sand Lake?"

"Absolutely," she replied, and led us the short distance to Sand Lake itself, a large and stationary body of water with nary a wave in sight. I removed my shoes and socks and rolled up my pants, figuring that Wimsey would appreciate the company seeing how eager he always was to drag me into bodies of water. We walked over to the lake and I waited for him to do what he normally did and plunge in. But Wimsey wasn't plunging anywhere. He stood quietly on the shore and gazed majestically into the distance like he was posing for his portrait.

"Look Wimsey, it's a lake!" I said and splashed him with some water to emphasize the point. He shook it back in my face and retreated to a drier distance. I waded in and tugged encouragingly at his leash. He inched forward to the water's edge. Then he bent down and had a drink. If he'd been any more bored he'd have been in the show ring. A human would've been checking their emails. I pulled out a piece of turkey and waved it at him. He walked in, snatched the turkey and then went to go shake lake water on Maria.

"I don't know what's wrong with him," I said to her. "There aren't any waves and he even tries to drag me into Bethesda Fountain and the toy boat pond in Central Park."

Maria pointed to my shoes and socks in full view on the shoreline.

"He knows you want him to go in."

As usual, she was right. Regular dogs have an uncanny knack for sensing when their humans want them to do something so they can do it; Wimsey had an uncanny knack for sensing when you wanted him to do something so he could refuse.

We made the remainder of the journey to Wimsey's family reunion with Wimsey stretched out across our laps. He was damp, smelly and snoring loudly. He obviously found not swimming very fatiguing.

As we got closer to Jan's I heard a familiar sound. It was faint at first but rose to a frenzied crescendo as soon as Trudy turned onto Jan's property. It was coming from a large fenced field inside of which stood a bellowing bevy of bloodhounds. Each seemed to be competing with the other in the warmth of their welcome.

Wimsey's head shot up like a rocket and was quickly followed by the rest of him as soon as Trudy opened the door.

I regained my footing and followed the others to a shady seating area under a tree.

"Wait here for a second," Jan said and disappeared into the small white house that stood adjacent to the field of Wimsey's dreams. When she returned she was holding the leash of Wimsey's father Stetson (Ch.Ewine and RamzyCreek's Walk on the Wild Side), a large and imposing red hound. Wimsey immediately tried to pay his filial respects to the parental rectum. Stetson immediately tried to pay his respects to Wimsey with his teeth.

"He's not good with strange male dogs," Jan informed us, a fact which seemed to have escaped Wimsey's notice. He exhibited a degree of valor wholly absent in his recent dealings with waves, rabbits or men doing tai chi. On the other hand, Wimsey also thought that socializing with hissing cats and small dogs with wrinkled noses and bared teeth was a good idea.

Jan handed Stetson's leash to Maria and went back inside and returned with Wimsey's accidental mother, the much more placid Rum of Ramsey Creek. Rum was a smaller hound, but she was black and tan like Wimsey and was as quiet as Stetson was loud. There was no question who Wimsey took after. Although not quite in everything. Stetson, unlike Wimsey, had been a successful show dog and had racked up multiple wins in both the breed and group rings. He also had a successful second career as a pediatric therapy dog, which was a source of ongoing disagreement between Maria and myself. Maria was usually the one who had no illusions about what Wimsey was capable of (hence her "this is Wimsey we're talking about)," but in this case she was convinced that Wimsey, like his father, would make a good therapy dog. Both she and the ASPCA's therapy dog instructor in whose class I assisted, were always urging me to sign Wimsey up for classes. But at least the instructor had an excuse—she'd never met him.

"I don't think Wimsey would do very well in the certification tests," I would tactfully observe to Maria whenever the subject came up. "And even if he passed those, he would still have to pass an obedience test." What Wimsey would do to a hospital room, let alone the person in it, was the stuff of nightmares.

"But you could work with him," she would argue.

Because that had worked out for me so well in the show ring, I thought. I usually just changed the subject.

I took some pictures of Wimsey and his family for the blog—being careful to keep him away from either end of Stetson—and then turned to Jan.

"Do you think I could use the field to take some pictures of Wimsey running around? Dog parks where we live don't allow intact males so he never gets to be off leash."

"Sure," she replied, "give me a sec," and she went off to clear the field of its houndy inhabitants.

When the coast was clear, I ushered Wimsey into the empty field and removed his leash.

"Go frolic Wimsey!" I squealed and ran up and down so he'd get the idea. Wimsey stared at me like a professor with some new and interesting specimen. Then he dropped his nose to the ground and began to take a lengthy and exceedingly unphotogenic olfactory inventory of the field. The probability of Wimsey frolicking in the field was about the same as him swimming in Sand Lake.

I gave up and went to join the others who were now sipping margaritas under the shady tree.

Jan handed me a drink and we began to discuss the events leading up to Wimsey's unexpected arrival.

"In his defense, Clare had only ever seen assisted breeding before where I had to encourage the males and help them find the right position and so forth," Jan explained. "And without my help he really didn't think that the boys would be bright enough to figure out what to do on their own."

To people unfamiliar with bloodhounds this might seem ludicrous but to us it made perfect sense. We, too, had cause to question Wimsey's intelligence and life skills on any number of occasions. Like when he thought he could fit through a cat flap or when he fled in terror from a measuring tape like it was an instrument of Satan.

"After the puppies were born," Jan continued, "we had to do DNA tests to sort out which puppies had which fathers. I'll go get them for you."

I looked at the papers Jan handed me. A puppy is allowed to have a single DNA base mismatch with its potential father because although these are rare, it's Nature's way of diversifying a gene pool. Two mismatches, however, indicate non-paternity. I scanned the list of Rum's puppies. All nine of them were Stetson's. Eight of them were a perfect match. The ninth had that rare and unique single base mismatch. Somehow it didn't take my degree in genetics to know which puppy that turned out to be. It was staring at me imperiously through the fence because it wished to be liberated.

We had a wonderful time talking to Jan and Trudy and in spite of all the non-swimming, non-frolicking and Dixie mounting we had enjoyed the day immensely. Having a bloodhound is a lot like being in a cult. People outside of it seldom understood. And sometimes you didn't either. Like when you set out for Central Park on a hot day but inexplicably find yourself taking a sweaty tour of the construction sites of the Far West Side instead because your bloodhound likes the way they smell.

We were also going to miss the Baymont Inn although Wimsey made it clear he did not share our high opinion of the establishment. He found the minibar snacks unappealing and the lack of adjoining rooms unacceptable. Whenever I tried to return to my room it required the skills of a defensive tackle to prevent him from joining me.

We left Grand Rapids early the next morning and although the drive through Ohio didn't improve the second time around, surprisingly, the Lord Amherst did. There was a much more congenial desk clerk on duty and the rooms he gave us were perfect. A single door led to a small vestibule with a bedroom on either side. Both bedrooms also had doors which meant that I could at least (in theory) keep Wimsey out of mine at bedtime but that until then he could roam freely between them.

"I'm almost done unpacking," Maria called out. "Can you go get some ice, I'm setting up the bar."

The setting up of the bar was a much-anticipated road trip ritual after the driving was done for the day but sharing of space with Wimsey was not. And we weren't the only ones who were excited by the bar since where there were cocktails there were also cocktail nuts. Wimsey loved cocktail nuts. He ate them one at a time and masticated each one for such an extended period that you would have thought he had a large chunk of chewy meat in his mouth. Considering how long it actually took him to eat a large chunk of chewy meat I would have been better off carrying a pack of peanuts into the show ring.

I grabbed the ice bucket and headed out in search of the ice machine. At the end of our long corridor, I happened to look down. There, heeling at my side with the silent stealth of a cheetah on the hunt, was Wimsey. It was the last place you would ever expect to find him. He looked up at me. He swished his tail. I had no idea what kind of fun he had in mind, but I strongly suspected in might involve chasing a large dog down a long corridor. I lunged for his collar, but where his collar should be, there was only dewlap. Wimsey was as naked as the day he was whelped. I grabbed onto his dewlap with both hands and tried to use it to get him to turn around. It was like trying to steer a large and unwilling ship against a heavy current. We were making slow progress when somewhere down the corridor a door opened. A woman emerged. She looked at me. She looked at Wimsey. She looked at the dewlap steering. Then she screamed and ran back inside and slammed the door. I could hear the chain.

Maria met us in the vestibule.

"What happened? I thought he was in your room."

"Well I thought he was in yours. And how did he open the front door? And don't say it."

She said it.

"Well, this is Wimsey we're talking about."

We both turned to look at him. He was standing in front of the cocktail nuts salivating profusely.

He was the Hound of Our Hearts.

THE END

APPENDIX--MEN ARE FROM MARS, WOMEN ARE FROM VENUS AND BLOODHOUNDS ARE FROM WHERE?

When I first met Wimsey everything about him intrigued me so I starting digging into the history of bloodhounds, about which, like many people, I knew nothing. I was surprised to learn that not only are bloodhounds a very old breed but that they are the foundation stock for all the other scent hounds--beagles, bassets, foxhounds, and the like. The origins of the bloodhound are a matter of some conjecture, but one version says that Frankish knights in the Middle East discovered the forerunner of the bloodhound as well as a white hound known as the Talbot Hound. They brought specimens of both hounds back to Europe and deposited them at the Monastery of St. Hubert (St. Hubert being the patron saint of hunters) in what is today Belgium.

The monks bred and perfected the early bloodhound and such was the prowess of its nose that the monks were obligated to send a pair of them annually to the King of France. The hounds were known then, and still are in French speaking countries, as the Chien de St. Hubert, or the St. Hubert dog. Although the Talbot Hound is extinct, the small patches of white that occasionally show up on a bloodhound's chest and paws bear testimony to the fact that its bloodlines were intermingled with those of the modern bloodhound.

The bloodhound arrived in England with William the Conqueror and his Norman knights in the 11th century and we know that by the 16th century they were well-established. A record of them appears in an inventory of dogs prepared by Elizabeth I's court physician, where they are listed as "Sanguinarius," the Latin for bloodhound.

While the origin of the name St. Hubert dog is clear, no one has determined definitively why the breed is known in English and Anglo-Saxon languages as the bloodhound. One theory holds that they acquired the name due to their skill in tracking wounded animals from a single spot of blood. In fact, Wimsey and I met a retired K9 police officer who told me how his bloodhound dragged him across Brooklyn and up a flight of stairs to the apartment door of a perpetrator after picking up the scent from a small drop of blood left at the crime scene. Another, and less grisly explanation for the name bloodhound is that under medieval sumptuary laws, the hounds could only be owned by those carrying the highborn bloodlines of the aristocracy, so called "people of the blood." Thus they became known as "hounds of the blood" or the "blooded hound."

Whatever the origins of the name, the monks clearly did a superb job. The over-active salivary glands enhance the scent and the long ears stir it up and into the nose. Bloodhounds have the most powerful sense of smell in the canine world and the evidence of its nose is admissible in a court of law. Historically, however, I like to think that the power of their noses made them the Ferrari of hunting hounds, although there is evidence that their function in the hunt was that of a "limier" or leash hound. In this capacity they would have been used to track game for capture and dispatch by packs of other more violent hounds. Bloodhounds also excel at tracking humans and were used for this purpose early on, much as they are today where their extraordinary abilities and determination save lives.

But wherever the breed originated, they have changed very little over the centuries and remain the same high drive dogs with the unrivaled passion for scent that enraptured the kings of France. It is a privilege and a joy to watch them work.

It should also be noted that bloodhounds not only have powerful noses but powerful personalities as well. They are all almost always larger than life characters— hugely energetic, frequently destructive even in adulthood, totally idiosyncratic and stubborn and opinionated to a fault.

Maria likes to say bloodhounds aren't for everyone.

I would add maybe not for anyone. But a sense of humor helps. ☺.

Made in the USA
Middletown, DE
25 September 2022

11218568R00215